Farm - Work
and Words

by Gregor MacGregor

Finavon Print & Design

First published in Great Britain in 2012
by Finavon Print & Design 3 Cadgers Path Finavon Angus DD8 3QB

Cover & Illustrations by Gregor MacGregor

Copyright: Gregor MacGregor

ISBN: 0-9541689-8-4

THE AUTHOR

I was born in the year 1931 into a family that eventually became made up of five boys and two girls. Father who was a Fife-shire dairy farmer unfortunately died when I was still at school — Mother died a year later.

Later on in life I worked on an uncle's dairy farm in Fife during school holidays and weekends where I learned to hand milk cows, and do odd jobs, like carting turnips and delivering churns of milk in the mornings to the local co-operative creamery. I also did some fieldwork with an iron-wheeled tractor.

After leaving school at 14 years of age, I took on my first full time job working for my uncle. My uncle engaged me to help in the byre that included milking the cows, doing orra-work and driving the orra-horse. Eventually I was driving a pair of horses.

At 19 years of age I was called up to do two years National Service with the Royal Air Force, and was trained as a radar mechanic on a radar station in Malta.

After getting demobbed from the R.A.F, I gave my uncle a hand with the grain and potato harvests before I took a fee on a large arable livestock farm in Perthshire where both horses and tractors were used to carry out the daily work. I worked on several farms in Perthshire.

Throughout my time on farms, apart from driving horses, tractors, and dairying, I've looked after suckler cows, breeding ewes, breeding sows and free-range poultry. As foreman on some farms I organised the staff to carry out the work to be done on a daily basis.

I finished my working days as Foreman on a college farm where I gained various certificates in agriculture, including a certificate in farm business management.

I retired from work in 1996. My pastimes include a daily walk and swimming. I also do painting, using different mediums, drawing, writing articles, short stories and composing poems. Some of my work has been exhibited and sold or published.

FOREWORD

When Clydesdale horses were used on farms in Scotland from around 1800, hitched to improved machines and implements, farming in Scotland began to produce more food for the increase in the human population and livestock.

The methods employed in carrying out similar tasks on farms in Scotland and the words or terms (terminology) used, varied between counties, areas and districts.

The skill and knowledge required to manage a stud for producing heavy work horses, a dairy herd, a suckler herd, a flock of sheep, a herd of pigs and a flock of poultry etc., and also for the feeding and management of stores, the name given to growing cattle, sheep and pigs to be kept for fattening, would need a lengthy writing exercise to do justice to the farmers, stockmen and stockwomen involved. This is just a brief overview.

A dairy enterprise used a variety of equipment. Many of the dairy farms made cream, butter and cheese products. It was a science that required sophisticated apparatus operated by adept people.

Some farms situated on the outskirts of cities and towns also produced vegetables and fruit.

The following pages are an account of farm work carried out throughout a year using horses and the skills of the farm-workers who handled the machines, implements and tools to do the many different jobs.

Gregor MacGregor.

CONTENTS

BUILDINGS REQUIRED FOR AN ARABLE BEEF CATTLE AND SHEEP FARM OR AN ARABLE DAIRY FARM
from around the 1900s to the 1950s.

The Farm-house - For the farmer and his family.
The Cottages - For married ploughmen, stockmen, orra-men, and their families.
The Bothy - For single ploughmen.
The Steading - which included stables, cart sheds, byres, cattle courts or reeds, turnip sheds, a feed barn, straw barn, granary and horse-mill gear shed. There was also a tool shed, Dutch barn for hay or straw, hay and straw lofts and an engine shed along with an implement shed, tractor shed and sheep pens or fanks etc. There was a milk house adjoining the farmhouse on a dairy farm where the milk was water-cooled before it went into large cans or churns, and a wash-house next door where the hot washing of the dairy dishes took place which included luggies, pails, flagons, sieves, the milk cooler and the large milk cans or churns, before they were put into sterilising steam chests.
The Close -The area between the back-door of the farmhouse, and the farm buildings, or the area between the buildings.
Stack yard - An area of land close to the farm buildings for building corn sheaves, loose hay and straw bunches into stacks.

STAFF REQUIRED FOR A LARGE ARABLE LIVESTOCK FARM

The grieve gave the horsemen their orders or jobs to be done in the stable at starting or yokin' time. Beginning with the foreman, then to the other horsemen -second, third, fourth, fifth and so on, followed by going to a smaller stable or tool shed to give the orra-squad their jobs to be done. Some grieves discussed the day's work with the farmer beforehand.

The foreman set the pace at work, and was responsible for time-keeping, finishing time and any break during work.

The other horsemen were expected to be as skilled as the fore-man and therefore capable of taking their turn at most jobs, especially ploughing, drilling (ridging), building stacks of corn sheaves, loose hay and bunches of straw.

Orra-men carried out a variety of tasks on a farm. The first orra-man often an ex-foreman could be required to drive a pair of horses.

The haflin - a youth who worked with the orra-squad when not carting with the orra-horse, or harrowing a field with a pair of horses.

The loon - A boy just left school, no older than fourteen years of age. Worked with the orra-squad. Sometimes he might do some carting work with the orra-horse.

The out-by workers were usually the wives or daughters of the ploughmen, stockmen or orra-men. On smaller farms an out-by worker might be employed doing tasks in the farmhouse on a wet day.

The cattleman was responsible for the fattening cattle, and the three or four milk cows that supplied the farmhouse and the farm staff with milk.

The cattle-orraman tending to a small herd might have to join the orra-squad in the middle of the forenoon, more so in the late spring when the cattle were turned out to grass.

The shepherd was responsible for the fattening hoggets and / or a flock of breeding ewes.

On a large stock-rearing farm where calves and lambs were produced, the staff was similar to that of a fattening cattle and sheep enterprise.

The maids - They were mostly employed in the farmhouse, but helped with the milking, on a dairy farm, and might assist with the hay and grain harvests etc.

Ploughman was the name given to an experienced farm-worker. However, a ploughman who looked after and drove a pair of horses was referred to as a horseman.

On a large dairy farm, a dairyman was employed. He would get assistance with the milking, especially if the cows were hand-milked. A shepherd would not normally be employed on a dairy farm, although there might be a small flock of breeding ewes looked after by the farmer. Large dairy and beef farms might have employed two dairymen or two cattlemen respectively.

On a smaller farm that might employ two horsemen, a cattleman or a dairyman and an out-by worker, the farmer would organise the tasks to be carried out by the staff, and left the foreman in charge while on business, attending the livestock market for instance. It wasn't unusual for a working farmer to carry out the same jobs as done by the farm staff.

A farmer's wife on a small or medium sized dairy farm would help with the milking of the cows, wash and steam the dairy dishes, and look after egg laying poultry such as hens, ducks and geese. Sometimes a maid was engaged to give the farmer's wife a hand, if the farmer and his wife had a young family.

CASUAL LABOUR

Casual or seasonal workers were added to the farm staff at certain times of the year. They helped with the potato planting in April, turnip singling in June, hay harvest in July, the grain harvest in September, the potato harvest in October and the turnip harvest during November. Irish and potato merchants' squads supplied a large number of the workers that included many women.

FOLK FOR THE THRESHING MILL

The large farms usually managed with very little help from outside where as the smaller farms in the same neighbourhood pooled their work forces when threshing of corn stacks was taking place in their area by a travelling threshing mill belonging to a contractor.

SCHOOL CHILDREN

On some farms, farmers' sons and farm workers' sons, helped around the farms at the weekends among the dairy cows, the beef cattle, sheep, pigs and hens etc. An able lad might get to cart turnips for instance. The older lassies that lived on the farm often helped with the farm work, or gave their mothers a hand in the house. Throughout the year when on holidays from school, the lads and lassies would be employed at the potato planting, the singling and weeding of turnips and the potato harvest etc.

THE MARRIED PLOUGHMAN

A married ploughman on a large arable livestock farm stayed in a cottage. Being a tied house, it meant that if he left his job or got sacked, he had to vacate the house for an incoming worker. The married ploughman usually stayed for a minimum of one year. He received potatoes, milk, oatmeal and sometimes paraffin oil for his household lamps. It depended on the agreement between the two parties. A married ploughman might be the foreman on the farm.

THE SINGLE PLOUGHMAN

On large arable livestock farms in certain districts of Scotland, five or six horsemen, and the foreman who was responsible for getting the men up in the morning, would live in a bothy. Some bothies had a bedroom for each man, or a communal room with beds in it for all the men. A big room furnished with a table, chairs and forms was where the lads had their meals. A large coal fire that heated the water was used for cooking on. A bathroom and toilet were also provided.

Many bothies, especially the smaller ones fell short of those standards as some had no water, and had to be collected from a water tap outside. The toilets were usually shared with the cattle in the cattle courts. In the larger bothies every man had to do his turn on pannie for a week. He was responsible for the fire, paraffin oil for the lamps, which he received from the grieve, and making the tea. He also had to make enough porridge in a large iron pot to do for breakfast and dinner at noon. He had to make sure that the flagons which were filled with milk, supplied by four or five cows on the farm, were on the table, each flagon beside a bowl of porridge, ready for the lads when they came back from the stable after attending to the needs of their pairs of horses. The man on pannie had to attend his horses between five, and five-thirty in the morning along with the rest of the lads, and leave the stable earlier to have the porridge ready for six-thirty.

Bothy lads were given milk, oatmeal, potatoes, coals and paraffin oil along with a wage to be paid, agreed by the farmer. Some grieves fee'd the men.

Flittings for married and single men were often done using a horse and cart. The single man loaded his two chests on at the railway station, closest to the farm he was leaving, to go by rail and be collected by horse and cart from the railway station nearest to the farm where he was engaged to work. One of his two chests was used for keeping his bowl, plate, cutlery and food in, while the other one was used for keeping his clothes in. Six months or a year was the usual length of time a single man stayed on a farm, although some lads stayed much longer.

A woman attended to the bothy every day or once a week. She would clean the bothy and make the beds. The woman doing the job might be the farmer's wife, the maid, a ploughman's wife or a stockman's wife. Each district or county had its own bothy systems. On the smaller farms the bothy lads had their meals in the farmhouse. Gradually bothies became empty by the 1970s.

Local railway stations took on the loading and unloading of goods such as livestock, animal feed, fertiliser and potatoes etc., to go or come by rail. The goods were either delivered or collected at the stations by the farm folk from nearby farms. Many railway stations were closed down by the 1960s.

DESCRIPTION OF HORSE IMPLEMENTS AND MACHINES USED THROUGHOUT A YEAR

The headings and texts can be compared with the appropriate illustrations.

The difference between implements and machines is that implements such as ploughs, harrows, discs, cultivators, grubbers, rollers, drill ploughs, hay sweeps and horse-drawn turnip hoes etc., have no gears, while machines such as corn drills, fertiliser distributors, double drillers, potato planters, turnip seeders, mowers, hay turners, binders and potato diggers etc. have gear wheels, sprockets and chains or pulleys and belts for operating the moving parts.

Ground-driven wheels are wheels that rotate because the implement or machine to which they belong is being pulled. Ground-driven wheels on most machines had sprockets or gear-wheels fixed to the inner side of the wheel hubs. By moving a lever on the machine, the gear wheel would engage another wheel, or the main sprocket would drive another sprocket by means of a chain. Some machines had through shafts from one ground-driven wheel to the other one with a bevel gear in the middle. The potato digger was an example. Depth-control wheels were fitted on most implements and machines.

THE PLOUGH

A single-furrow plough pulled by a pair of horses was made up of an iron beam at the front, a metal mould board next, and a pair of wooden or iron stilts at the rear, which the ploughman used for controlling the plough. On the beam were fixed a depth-control wheel, and an adjustable coulter that cut into the soil just above the share, an extension to the mould board.

A chain fixed on the end of the beam was hooked on at the middle of a large swingle- tree, a wooden bar with metal links at either end. It was then hitched to two smaller swingle - trees. They in turn were hitched to draught chains that were hooked on to tug hooks on the hames that were fixed to the collars on a pair of horses. This type of hitching up or yoking was common on most farms. The large swingle tree was called the master tree or yoke.

Coulters were variable. There were cutting discs, skimmers (like miniature ploughs) and the original coulter, a thick blade with a cutting edge.

At one time ploughs were made of wood as with other implements. Harrows for example.

A double-furrow plough that was pulled by three horses was not as common as the single-furrow plough that required two horses to pull it.

A reversible single-plough pulled by two horses was even more rare.

Nowadays a plough that is not reversible is called a conventional plough.

Two distinct furrows were made in ploughing, a whole furrow made by a long mould board with little concavity, was unbroken, while a broken furrow made by a short mould board with a more concave shape, inverted the furrow with a pulverising effect.

Some ploughs had a furrow wheel and a land wheel while some had a land wheel only. Swing ploughs didn't have a wheel. They were the most difficult to control whilst ploughing.

When ploughing a grass field for instance, good tight ploughing was essential so as to prevent the corn seeds, sometimes sown by hand, from falling down between the furrows. After the seed was sown, the field was harrowed across the ploughing and finally rolled. When the field of grain was well sprouted, the result of the ploughman's work could be seen - continuous straight green lines, evenly spaced.

HARROWS

Harrows were usually pulled by a pair of horses, and were normally made up of two, three, four or five leaves or sections, depending on the type of soil, and the weight of the harrows. Clay soil required heavy harrows, two leaves only, whereas harrowing grass seed into the soil, could be done with five lighter leaves.

The leaves were zigzag shaped, and meshed neatly when laid out side by side on the ground. This ensured that no piece of ground was missed if two adjoining leaves were slightly parted caused by a stone, or an uneven piece of ground when harrowing.

DISC-HARROWS OR DISCS

Disc-harrows were pulled by two or three horses. They were made up of ten or twelve concave shaped discs positioned at the rear of the machine, and a pair of medium sized wheels set three feet apart at the front supported a beam which joined a cross beam that held the discs in place, A seat was provided for the ploughman with a handle close at hand to enable him to alter the cut or angle of the discs.

ROLLERS

There were various types of rollers.

A plain light roller pulled by one horse.

A plain heavy roller was pulled by a pair of horses in chains, with a pole fixed to the roller going up between the horses to be attached to the bottom of their collars by chains or leather straps.

A Cambridge roller was pulled by one horse, and was made up of rings with a flange in the middle of each ring. This helped to break up small clods prior to sowing seed, or after the sowing and harrowing was completed.

A heavy roller was pulled by three horses, and was made up of thick rings with cone-shaped lugs spaced around the rim. It was mainly used on clay soils.

CULTIVATORS AND GRUBBERS

There were various types of cultivators and grubbers, some ran on two large wheels at the rear and a smaller wheel at the front, pulled by two or three horses using draught chains, and others ran on two wheels only, pulled by two horses using a pole and chains. A seat was provided for the horseman with a lever close at hand to enable him to set the working depth required for the machine, and to lift the tines or stangs clear off the ground before turning on the end-rig, for instance. Some of them could be adapted to grub between the potato drills, doing three drills in one pass by altering the stangs on the frame. The stangs were fitted with broad shares called ducks' feet, and set in a staggered pattern to ensure good soil flow. They were always set this way whether cultivating or grubbing. Narrower shares were used for cultivating. As cultivators and grubbers became one of the same, cultivating the land was done before the potatoes were planted, and grubbing was done between the rows, after the potatoes were planted and growing.

SINGLE ROW POTATO GRUBBER

A single row grubber pulled by a pair of horses using draught chains had five stangs fitted with broad shares, one stang was at the front behind a small depth control wheel, and the other four were in pairs, the middle pair set in a staggered pattern. The horseman controlled it from the rear by the use of handles similar to a plough.

DRILL PLOUGH

A drill plough pulled by a pair of horses was similar in design to an ordinary plough except that it had a mould board on either side enabling it to make ruts for potatoes to be planted in, or ridges for sowing turnip seed on.

COMMENCING THE YEAR WITH EARLY SPRING WORK

Carting large stones off the ploughed fields before cultivations took place. Couch grass was dug up around the edges and corners of the fields, and loaded on to carts and dumped in a suitable place.

Filling in finishes using a plough. It made the field level throughout, enabling implements and machines to travel across the field without being damaged.

SPREADING SLAG, LIME AND FERTILISER

Slag was spread on grass fields using a fertiliser spreader or distributor pulled by one horse. Slag improved grasses and clovers.

Lime, a white powdery substance when broken down from lumps. It was spread from carts or heaps in the field. Spreading lime is now carried out using spreaders hitched to tractors. Lime was spread on fields found to be high in acidity.

Fertiliser was spread on fields using a spreader. One type used consisted of a long metal hopper that held the fertiliser, and sat between two large ground-driven wheels, with a row often or twelve dished plates rotating slowly at the bottom of the hopper. Each plate filled with fertiliser protruded about halfway at the rear of the machine where a spindle with small tines or "fingers" flicked the fertiliser out of the plates on to the ground.

Wheel tracks made by carting stones from fields, spreading lime and fertiliser were grubbed out using a cultivator or a grubber.

EXTRA TREATMENT TO GRASS FIELDS

A chain harrow pulled by a single horse was used on grass fields. The harrow consisted of one complete large square made up of small triangle links with short spikes linked together. The short spikes pulled the old withered grasses out, and also spread any dung left by grazing animals. This job was usually done in February, although it could be carried out throughout the year.

Dairy cows' wash or urine was sprayed on grass fields using a wash cart. It consisted of a large wooden barrel lying sideways fixed on a frame made of wood with shafts attached to it to enable it to be pulled by one horse. The wash flowed from the barrel into a "T" piece fixed to it. The top of the "T" being the boom that was about six feet long from which the wash came out from holes spaced along the underside of the boom at the rear of the cart. The wash was collected in a large tank, and pumped manually into the barrel of the wash cart. Spraying was carried out throughout the year.

Dung was also put on some grass fields by pulling dung out thinly from a moving cart using a muck hack. After a field was completely dunged, it was harrowed to ensure the dung covered the ground more evenly.

SOWING BARLEY AND OAT SEEDS

By using harrows, a field could become ideal for sowing cereal seeds. The seed was sown by a corn drill or seeder pulled by two or three horses. The corn drill was made up of a metal or wooden hopper that sat between two large ground-driven wheels. Small wheels fixed along the bottom of the hopper pushed the seeds out through small holes where they fell down inside hoses or tubes attached to disc coulters which made grooves for the seeds to finally settle in. Short small chains fixed at the rear of the eleven or more coulters, covered the seeds with soil. After the field was sown it was harrowed and rolled.

To ensure that the field was sown at the correct seed rate, many machines didn't have acre counters fitted on them, so sacks or bags of seed grain were set out against the fence, dyke or hedge-side along one of the end-rigs. The distance between them was stepped out in so many yards by the grieve. The horseman would be expected to have sown all the seed in the sacks by finishing time. Sowing normally commenced at a long straight side of a field and progressed to the other side. The end-rig was usually sown last.

ROLLING GRASS FIELDS

Rolling grass fields for grazing were rolled in early spring, depending on the weather and growth of grass. Fields for a hay crop were usually done later on when the grass was a bit longer. This enabled the horseman to see the mark made by the edge of the roller on the previous pass. It ensured all stones were rolled in flush with the surface, thus preventing machines from getting damaged. Any large stones were put into a box fitted to the frame of the roller.

SOWING GRASS SEED

Every year, two or three fields were sown with a grass seed mixture. It was sown on fields already sown to grow barley or oat crops. This was done to replace old grass fields already ploughed up for cropping, which helped to keep the rotation of crops in the right order.

A grass seed broadcaster pulled by a single horse was used for doing the job. It ran on two wheels with two long hoppers or boxes positioned above them. Sacks of seed were laid out along the end-rig in a similar way to the sacks of corn. When sowing was being carried out the seed was agitated by "fingers" attached to the spindles that sat along the bottom of each box. This caused the seed to fall on to the ground from a row of small holes on the underside of each box. After the fields were sown, they were harrowed with lightweight harrows and rolled. The hoppers on the broadcaster were turned parallel to one another for transporting through gates.

Sometimes the grass seed was sown after a grain crop was well established. This was to ensure that the young grass would not be too lush at harvest time, thus preventing the sheaves from having too much grass at the butt ends, damp canvases and blockages at the knife-bar on the binder. Fields sown with grass seed in this way were also harrowed and rolled.

WINTER WHEAT

Winter wheat that had been sown the previous backend was harrowed and rolled.

Fertiliser was spread on the field, as the crop would be growing vigorously after being dormant most of the winter.

PREPARING GRASS FIELDS FOR CATTLE TURNOUT

REPAIRING FENCES

Before cattle were turned out to grass from the cattle courts in April-May, fences around the fields were checked, and repaired by replacing rotting and broken stobs or posts. Strainers, large round posts found at gateways, and at certain points on a fence along with rances or stays were checked and replaced if necessary.

Wires were tightened up and replaced if need be. Missing staples on strainers and posts were replaced. Broken spars were replaced on gates.

REPAIRING DYKES

Dry stone dykes built up where parts had fallen down. Coping -stones might just require righted up, and packed tightly. Plain or barbed wire held up by short metal posts above low dykes was checked and made taut if necessary.

DRINKING WATER FOR LIVESTOCK

Water troughs in fields were cleaned out, and water turned on at the tobies that were usually close to the troughs. This was done to check if the ball cocks in the troughs were working properly, so preventing the water from running over the sides.

Step stones were laid at parts of the troughs to give sheep easy access to water. Watering holes in ditches and burns were made free of silt and stones to give livestock, especially cattle, a reasonable depth of water to drink from.

POTATO PLANTING

The ground was prepared for potato planting by harrowing or disc - harrowing followed by deep cultivating. It was finally harrowed and drilled or ridged up, using a drill plough pulled by a pair of horses. The fertiliser was spread on the fields either during the cultivations, or after the ridging was completed. Another way of making drills for potato planting was done by a double driller pulled by a pair of horses. It was made up of a wooden hopper that held fertiliser, and sat between two large ground-driven wheels. A small rudder wheel with a middle flange around the rim was situated at the front of the machine from which a rudder handle fixed to an upright from the small wheel, reached across the hopper, handy for the horseman walking behind the machine. It was used to ensure the horseman kept the machine on a straight course, by using a mark made on the ground from the previous pass by one of the two markers fixed on either side of the machine. Fertiliser from the hopper went down two spouts into a rut each, made by two small ridging ploughs attached to the underside of the main frame. On some farms dung from a moving cart was put into the bottom of the drills before planting of potatoes commenced.

Potato planting was done by potato merchants' squads and Irish squads. It was also carried out by local folk, farm folk and the oldest school children on their two weeks holidays in April. The planters who belonged to potato merchants and Irish squads were mostly females, and the smaller local squads were made up of women and the older school lassies and laddies.

Planters carried potatoes in aprons by folding the apron up to waist height to form a "hammock", and holding the two comers of the apron together with one hand. They then used the other hand to drop the potatoes into the rut or bottom of the drills. Some planters preferred an apron that resembled a pouch to hold the potatoes.

The gaffer in charge of the squad walked behind the line of planters that could number thirty or more. He checked out the spacing of the potatoes in each drill. He might have to tell a planter or planters to plant the potatoes closer together or wider apart. The spacing could be around nine inches.

The planters were kept supplied with potatoes from three or four men using baskets. Men required for the job depended on how many planters were in the squad. Each man would fill a basket from a hundredweight (50kgs) sack of potatoes and share it with three or four planters. Single bags of potatoes were spaced, say at fifteen yards apart atop every twelfth drill. Measurements varied according to the seed size and the spaces being made between the potatoes by the planters. The standard distance between each drill was twenty-eight inches.

After planting was well underway, drill ploughs pulled by horses were used to cover the potatoes by splitting the drills.

One or two row horse drawn potato planters were used on some farms during the 1930s. The hoppers that held the potatoes sat between two skeletal ground-driven wheels designed to sit on top of the drills.

Plough with implements and machines required for a grain crop to be grown

Single furrow plough
with two wheels

Harrows (3-leaves)

Discs

Corn drill (seeder)

Fertiliser spreader

Plain roller

Cambridge roller

Most horse machines and implements were no wider than about 10 feet

19

IMPLEMENTS USED IN PREPARING THE GROUND FOR GROWING POTATOES AND TURNIPS

CULTIVATOR

SPRING TINED CULTIVATOR

GRUBBER

SOME GRUBBERS COULD BE SET FOR GRUBBING BETWEEN THE POTATO DRILLS

Implements and Machine used for making drills (ridges) for potato planting and turnip seed sowing

DEPTH CONTROL WHEEL

Two mould boards adjustable to make wide or narrow tops

MARKER CAN BE SWUNG OVER THE TOP OF THE DRILL PLOUGH FOR THE RETURN PASS WHEN DRILLING

SINGLE DRILL PLOUGH

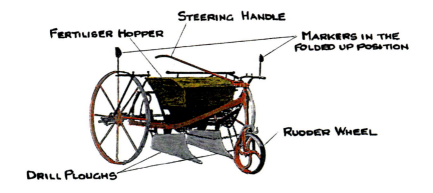

STEERING HANDLE

FERTILISER HOPPER

MARKERS IN THE FOLDED UP POSITION

RUDDER WHEEL

DRILL PLOUGHS

DOUBLE DRILLER

TOOL BAR OR FRAME DESIGNED TO TAKE GRUBBER TINES

THREE DRILLER

Machine and Implements
Required for Growing a Potato Crop

Potato cups

Potato hoppers

Wheels designed to sit on top of the drills

Potatoes released from the cups at the bottom of the funnels.

There were also one row planters.

Most farmers used squads to do their potato planting

Potato planters became popular with the arrival of tractors

Two row potato planter

After the potatoes were planted the drills were soon harrowed (pulled down) and ridged (run up) again. This continued until the white stems on the potatoes appeared above the surface.

Potato drill harrows or saddle harrows

Depth control wheel.

Plates. Duck foot shaped.

Single row potato grubber

Machine and Implements
required for growing a turnip crop

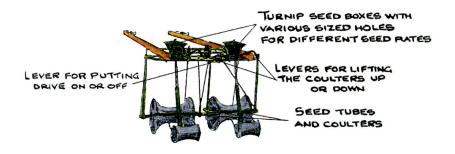

Turnip seed boxes with
various sized holes
for different seed rates

Lever for putting
drive on or off

Levers for lifting
the coulters up
or down

Seed tubes
and coulters

Turnip seeder
or neep barrie

Levers for lifting
and lowering the discs
They can also shift the discs side-ways

Scarifier

Lever for adjusting
the working width of
the tines

Depth control wheel

"A" shaped plate

"L" shaped plates

Horse turnip hoe

Machines and Implements

Grass seed broadcaster

Markers - Usually worn plough shares

Chain harrows

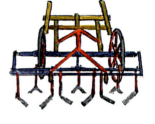

3. Row horse hoe

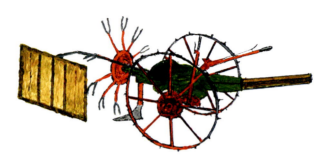

Potato digger

An endless chain with cups attached to it travelled up through part of the hopper sectioned off, and picked up potatoes on the way up, a potato in each cup, and deposited the potatoes on the way down into a funnel which led the potatoes to the bottom of a drill at the required spacing.

SOWING TURNIP SEED

The ground was prepared for turnip seed sowing by disc- harrowing, harrowing, deep cultivating, harrowing and finally rolling. Fertiliser was spread on the field to allow ridging to commence. Cultivations were variable, depending on soil type etc.

Sowing turnip seed was carried out using a two-drill turnip-seeder pulled by one horse. It ran on two concave shaped rollers that firmed up the drill tops. Seeds from two metal boxes situated on a frame above the rollers, were pushed out through a hole by brushes fixed on thin spindles inside each box, and fell down inside tubes into narrow grooves made by two coulters. Behind each coulter was a small plain roller that firmed the soil covering the seed.

Another way was to use a double driller with fertiliser, and split the drills with a drill plough before sowing the turnip seed. This helped to keep the maximum amount of fertiliser close to the growing turnip.

Finally, a method used on some farms was to drill the field using a double-driller without fertiliser. Dung was put into the bottom of the drills before splitting the drills with a drill plough. This kept the dung close to the growing plants.

CARTING STONES OFF GRAIN FIELDS

After the young plants were well established in the cornfields, stones were gathered up and thrown into carts travelling the same way as the field was sown. Two or three carts might be used. The loaded carts were taken to a suitable dumping ground where the stones were un-loaded, to be used at a later date to mend field roads etc.

ROWCROP WORK AMONG THE POTATO DRILLS

Harrowing down potato drills and ridging them up again for weed control would start a week or two after the potato planting was completed, and would continue until white stems appeared at one stage of harrowing. Harrowing was done using two saddle shaped harrows linked together, pulled by one horse. The horseman controlled the harrows by holding a handle from each harrow as he walked between them. Two drills were harrowed in one pass. Chain harrows could do the job. Eventually grubbing between the rows of potatoes took place after leaves began to appear.

MIDDENING DUNG

As the cattle had been turned out to the grass fields during April/ May, the cattle courts empty off livestock, were ready for mucking out. The dung was loaded in to coup carts using graips. The horsemen received help from some of the orra-squad to load the carts that were taken to a field where the midden was being made on an end-rig near a gateway. On top of the midden would be the remainder of the orra-squad spreading the loads of dung. A trace horse was used to help pull the loaded carts up on to the midden.

CLEANING, WHITE-WASHING AND PAINTING

After the cattle courts were mucked out, brushing rafters, scraping walls and floors was carried out. This was followed by white washing the walls with lime which had been big lumps, bubbling away in an old bath of water until it became a cold white liquid ready for using with a broad hand brush. Stables, byres, and loose boxes etc. were white-washed. Paint and creosote was applied where appropriate. Lead in paint was a problem especially where calves were concerned.

Carts, wooden wheelbarrows, doors, rones and rone-pipes etc. were also cleaned and painted, although some of them might not be done every year.

SCARIFYING THE TURNIP DRILLS

To prepare the drills for singling the turnips, an implement called a scarifier was used, pulled by a single horse. The implement ran on four wheels angled on one side to suit the shape of the drills, and just behind the wheels were four large concave shaped discs, two to a drill, which pared the soil away from the sides of the drills to leave a ridge of plants ready for singling. It pared two drills in one pass.

TURNIP SINGLING

Using a hand hoe, turnip singling was done by scraping down evenly on both sides of a drill at a proper angle to from a neat ridge leaving the singled plants approximately nine inches apart. Unwanted plants should have finished up between the drills with the roots free of most of the earth, so as not to encourage the possible re-growth of those plants, especially when hoeing in wet conditions. Many farms required help from Irish or potato merchants' squads to get the job done before the plants became too large and difficult to single. Numbers in a squad varied. On large farms the staff could supply up to fifteen or more folk for the hoeing.

Many women were involved at the singling of the turnips.

Turnip singling competitions were held in some parts of Scotland during the evenings.

In some counties or districts, folk singled the plants by hand whilst on their knees. Hessian sacking wrapped around the legs up past the knees offered some physical protection for the legs.

MOWING GRASS FOR A HAY CROP

A mower pulled by a pair of horses was used to mow or cut the grass. It ran on two wheels that drove the gearing to a crank-shaft or pitman which caused the knife, a slim bar with a row of "V" shaped cutting sections riveted to it, to reciprocate through a row of fingers fixed to a long flat plate known as the knife bar. At the outer end of the knife bar was a small depth control wheel bolted on to a bracket that held a wooden shedder that turned the edge of the swath of grass inwards to make a clear strip between each swath. At the inner end of the knife bar was a larger depth control wheel. The knife bar could be lifted clear of the ground by using a lever situated next to a seat provided for the horseman. A short lever was also used to engage or disengage the gear drive. For transporting through gates for instance, the knife bar could be folded up. Mowing the field was done by mowing a wide end rig first, then mowing round about or in strips, depending which way the crop was lying over.

TURNING HAY

Turning the swaths of hay over was done by a single horse-drawn hay-turner that turned two swaths over in one pass. It ran on two large wheels that supplied the drive to the two reels at the rear of the machine that were made off sprung steel tines. A seat was provided for the horseman with a lever near at hand for putting the drive to the reels on or off. A baffle plate was situated to one side of each reel to make the swaths sit up as this let the wind dry the hay quicker.

Another way of turning hay was done by a squad of folk pushing the shafts of their forks along the ground at a good walking pace, turning the swaths over and exposing the undersides to the sun and wind.

TEDDING HAY

Some farms had single horse-drawn tedders that ran on two medium sized wheels that spanned the swath to be tedded or shaken out. The swath picked up by curved tines fitted to bars on a rotor, went round over the top to be laid on to the ground again more spread out. A canopy, open at the rear of the machine, along with a pulley and belt drive made the machine complete. The belt was tightened to drive the rotor. The horseman drove the horse while walking at the side of the tedder.

ADDITIONAL JOBS DONE DURING MAY, JUNE AND JULY

Row-crop work continued among the potato drills before any damage was done to the haulms. Furrowing up was finally done when the soil was a bit damp as this ensured the drills kept their shape, and prevented greening of exposed tubers until lifting time.

The haulms were kept free of earth while furrowing up to prevent them from being "hung", so curtailing the growth of the crop.

HORSE-HOEING TURNIPS

Weeding between the turnip drills would be going on using a single-row horse hoe, pulled by one horse, similar in design to a potato grubber, but not so heavy. Four shares were "L" shaped, two left-handed and two right-handed, were fitted on to four upright stangs to weed and pare the soil away from the plants. The single stang at the front was fitted with an "A" shaped share that weeded in the middle between the drills. Hoeing was done just below the surface.

A three-row horse hoe was used on some farms. Pulled by one horse it ran on two medium sized wheels. Shares were similar to the ones fitted to a single row hoe. The horseman walked at the rear between two handles that were used to lift the shares to clear a blockage caused by weeds or stones. A locking catch was used to keep the shares up for transporting. Hoeing would continue before damage was done to the plants.

SECOND HOEING TURNIPS AND HOEING POTATOES

Second hoeing of turnips was done when the plants were quite large and weeds were appearing in numbers around the young turnips. A squad of folk would do the job with each person walking between two drills, and hoeing the one on their left first, or vice-versa if left-handed, and turn at the end of the drill and hoe the other drill on the way back to the other end of the field. The soil was pushed away from the plants when weeding, as this encouraged the growth of the bulbs to become large turnips in November.

Hoeing potato drills was done using much the same procedure as hoeing turnips except the soil was pulled up to the plants to ensure the small tubers and stems were adequately covered with earth. Hence the maxim - "hunger a neep and feed a tattie."

Sometimes weeding of turnips and potatoes was done by hand whilst folk were on their knees. Hessian sacking wrapped around their legs up passed the knees offered some protection for the legs.

TUMBLING TAM

When the hay was ready to be built into coles or rucks, tumbling tams or hay sweeps were used to supply hay to the squads building the crop into coles or rucks. Pulled by one horse using draught chains, the tumbling tam was made up of seven wooden tines fixed to a thick wooden back stick from which two stilts or handles were attached. After a sweep-full of hay had been collected, the horseman stopped and backed the horse, then pulled the sweep back about a yard and let go the handles, got the horse to move on, and then he walked beside the sweep as it tumbled over leaving the hay next to a cole or ruck being built. The horseman moved back in behind the sweep, gripped the handles and carried on to collect more hay. Two or three hay sweeps would be required on a large farm. Wider hay sweeps required a horse on either side to pull them.

COLES AND RUCKS

Coles were small cone shaped stacks of hay that had nine feet tall wooden tripods in the middle of them. This helped in the maturing and drying of the crop.

After the coles were built they were raked down, and the long ends were pulled out from around the bottom of them as this prevented wastage when the coles settled down among the grass that was sure to grow to a good height before they were removed from the field in about three weeks time. The coles were also cross roped over the top with esparto grass rope, and the ends of the ropes tied round wisps of hay then tucked into the hay near the bottom of the coles.

Rucks which were built without large tripods inside them, were raked and roped in a similar fashion to the coles.

HORSE-RAKE

A horse-rake pulled by one horse was about nine feet wide, made of iron and ran on two large wheels. It was made up of a row of thin curved tines, and a seat was provided for the horseman to enable him to operate a dump pedal or hand lever to lift the tines clear off the ground,

Machines and Implements
for making hay.

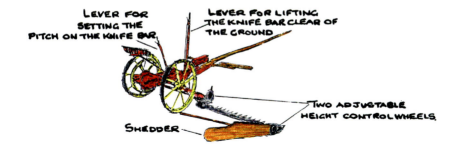

Lever for setting the pitch on the knife bar.

Lever for lifting the knife bar clear of the ground

Two adjustable height control wheels.

Shedder

Hay mower - right-hand cut.
Left-hand cut mowers were also available

Hay turner
It could be adjusted to tedd (tease out) the hay

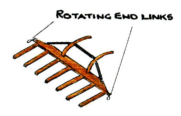

Rotating end links

Tumbling Tam
or hay sweep

Hay tedder

Lever for lifting tines clear of the hay when making rows

Horse rake

USING A HAY BOGIE FOR CARTING (LEADING) HAY RUCKS

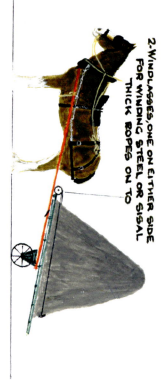

2 - WINDLASSES, ONE ON EITHER SIDE
FOR WINDING STEEL OR SISAL
THICK ROPES ON TO

HAY RUCK LOADED ON TO HAY BOGIE

CLEEKS ON END
OF EACH ROPE
HOOKED TOGETHER

DETATCHABLE WHEEL
WITH HANDLE FOR
WINDING ON HAY RUCK

LEVER FOR RELEASING CATCH TO ENABLE FLOOR TO BE TILTED

HAY RUCK READY TO BE WOUND ON TO HAY BOGIE

32

BUILDING ROUND HAY-STACKS

USING A HORSE FORK

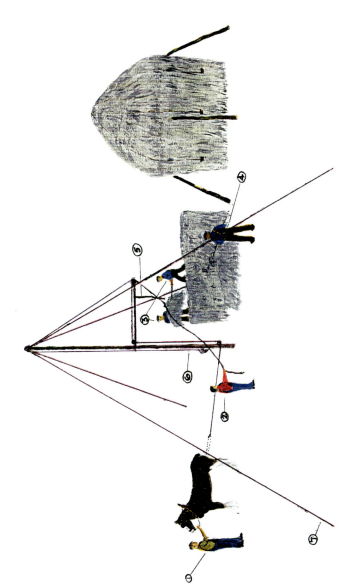

1. MAN DRIVING HORSE BACKWARDS AND FORWARDS TO RAISE AND LOWER THE FORK.
2. WOMAN TO TUG TRIP ROPE ON FORK WHEN CALLED TO DO SO.
3. BUILDER AND ASSISTANT PUSHING SLAG OF HAY INTO POSITION BEFORE CALLING ON THE WOMAN TO TUG THE TRIP ROPE ON THE FORK.
4. MAN WHO PUSHES FORK INTO RUCK OR COLE FOR GRABBING A SLAG OF HAY.
5. ROPE FOR PULLING JIB OVER THE STACK.
6. ROPE FOR RAISING OR LOWERING THE JIB
7. ONE OF FOUR GUY ROPES.

The Binder
showing crop flow

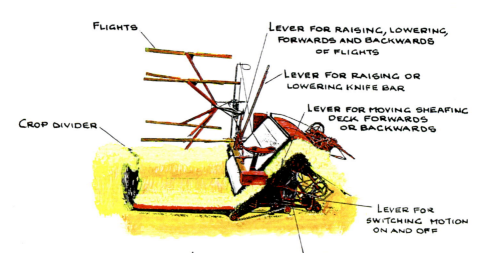

Flights

Lever for raising, lowering, forwards and backwards of flights

Lever for raising or lowering knife bar

Lever for moving sheafing deck forwards or backwards

Crop divider

Lever for switching motion on and off

Large ground driven wheel supplying the motion through-out the binder by sprocket wheels chains and gear wheels

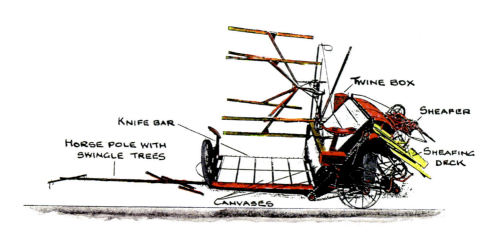

Twine box

Sheafer

Knife bar

Horse pole with swingle trees

Sheafing deck

Canvases

The Binder
ready for transporting

On a very hot sunny day straw could become very slippy especially barley and wheat sheaves. The stacker had to keep a grip - build bare to prevent the side of the stack slipping out completely.

BOSS (TRIPOD)

A set is made up of one stacker, carters and in the field, forkers and cart builders. On large arable farms three or four sets were common.

Sets worked in pairs. Two forkers would pass sheaves to two stackers (a stack each) from the same side of the loaded cart.

Stacks were often built in fields near a gate. It allowed the threshing mill easy access to the stacks which were always built in two rows with a road in between, to allow the threshing mill to thresh out the stacks from both sides.

Stackyards were usually used for wheat stacks built on stathels, some oat stacks and hay stacks.

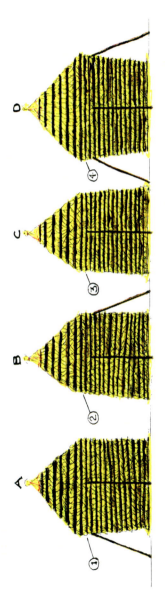

A good stacker would have noticed when building a stack.

A1 - Heavy side would be lower. The stack would be losing its roundness and be off centre.

B2 - Light side would be higher. The stack would be losing its roundness and be off centre.

C3 - Bare or light all round. The roundness (circumference) in size would be decreasing.

D4 - Heavy all round. The roundness in size would be increasing.

35

COMPLETE ELEVATION

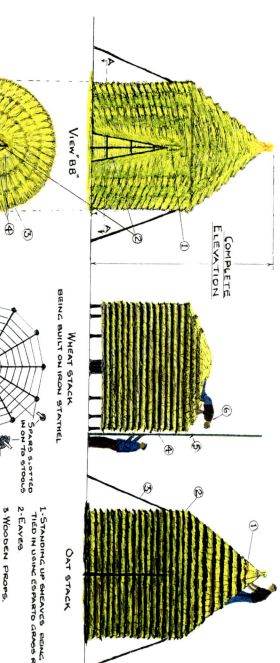

VIEW "BB"

VIEW "AA"

1-HOLE- An arm's length deep to avoid stack settling on top of the BOSS (TRIPOD)

2-BOSS - Made of wood

3-Outside layer built with a good slope to prevent water seeping into the stack.

4-All inside layers (THE HEART) built firmly and above the level of the respective outer layer. Heads of sheaves are kept slightly back-most.

PLAN OF IRON STATHEL

RADIAL SPARS HOOKED ON

SPARS SLOTTED IN ON TO STOOLS

WHEAT STACK BEING BUILT ON IRON STATHEL

OAT STACK

1-Standing up sheaves being tied in using esparto grass rope.

2-Eaves

3-Wooden props.

4-Wooden ladder.

5-Piece of string tied to rung of ladder. Height of eaves is measured this way to ensure all stacks settle down to a uniform height.

6-Stack builder checking the string against side of stack.

36

ROUND STACKS

with the props removed

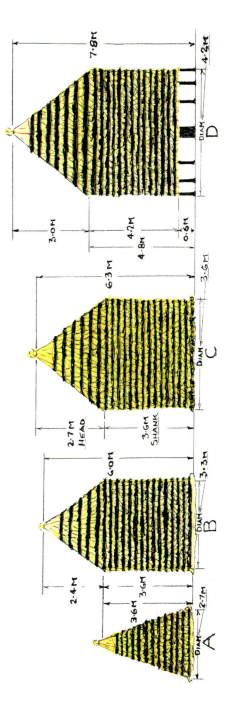

(Dimensions labeled on diagrams)

A — DIAM 2·7M; 3·6M; 2·4M

B — DIAM 3·3M; 6·0M; 3·6M SHANK, 2·7M HEAD

C — DIAM 3·6M; 6·3M; 3·6M SHANK, 2·7M HEAD

D — DIAM 4·2M; 0·6M; 4·8M; 4·2M; 3·0M; 7·8M

ALL MEASUREMENTS APPROXIMATE AND VARIABLE

TO CONVERT TO FEET DIVIDE BY 0·3

A - FRANDIE - BUILT WITH A BOSS (TRIPOD) IN THE MIDDLE - CROP VERY DAMP (IN POOR ORDER) WHEN DRIED AND THRESHED GRAIN WILL DO FOR FEED. STRAW USED FOR FEED AND BEDDING. FOUNDATION - STRAW

B - BARLEY STACK - BUILT WITH A BOSS IN THE MIDDLE. CROP IN GOOD ORDER. GRAIN USED FOR SEED, FEED AND MALTING (BREWING) STRAW FOR FEED AND BEDDING. FOUNDATION - STRAW

C - OAT STACK. BUILT WITH A BOSS IN THE MIDDLE. CROP IN GOOD/FAIR ORDER. GRAIN USED FOR SEED, FEED AND MILLING. STRAW FOR FEED AND BEDDING. FOUNDATION - STONES OR STRAW.

D - WHEAT STACK - CROP IN GOOD/FAIR ORDER. GRAIN USED FOR SEED, FEED AND MILLING. STRAW USED FOR THATCHING STACKS AND COVERING POTATO PITS (CLAMPS) TO KEEP THE CROP FROST FREE. WAS USED FOR BEDDING AFTER DISCARDED FROM PITS AND STACKS. FOUNDATION - STATHEL OR STRAW. BOSS NOT NORMALLY USED.

NOTE - IF STACK SETTLED DOWN EVENLY, ALL PROPS COULD BE TAKEN AWAY. HOWEVER, PROPS WERE USUALLY LEFT IN. TIGHTENED OR SLACKENED WHERE NEEDED. FRANDIES DIDN'T REQUIRE PROPS

ROPE ENDS TIED ROUND
A HANDFUL OF SHEAF
STALKS AND TUCKED INTO
SIDE OF STACK

THATCH

SHEAVES

1- TAPPIE - MADE OF WHEAT STRAW.
2- THATCH - WHEAT STRAW.
3- ESPARTO GRASS ROPES.
4- PROPS - WOODEN, 4 TO EACH STACK.
5- FOUNDATION - LOOSE STRAW.
6- LOOSE STRAW SWITCHED OFF THATCH.
7- BAND OF CHAIN-DISCARDED WHEN THATCHING, COMPLETED PIECE OF STRING THEN TIED AROUND THE TOP OF THE THATCH.

8- SWITCH - PIECE OF TREE BRANCH FOR SWITCHING (SWEEPING) LOOSE STRAW OFF THATCH.
9- GRAIP FOR HOLDING BUNCH OF WHEAT STRAW.
10- LONG WOODEN LADDER.
11- GRAIP FOR SECURING LADDER.
12- BUNCH OF WHEAT STRAW.
13- PITCH-FORK USED FOR PASSING BUNCHES UP TO THE MAN THATCHING THE STACK.
14- TAPPIE - MADE OF WHEAT STRAW.
15- BALLS OF ESPARTO GRASS ROPE.

Oblong Stack (Leet) Thatched
Ring Roped and Props Removed

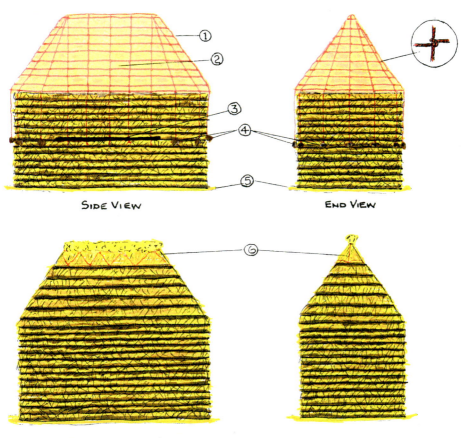

SIDE VIEW

END VIEW

LEET UNTHATCHED

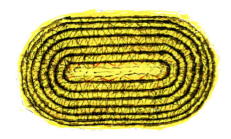

PLAN VIEW

1 - Esparto grass rope.
2 - Thatch - Wheat straw.
3 - Rope ends tied round props. which are used as weights
4 - Rope ends tied round bricks or stones which are used as weights.
5 - Foundation. Loose straw.
6 - Standing up sheaves tied in with esparto grass rope.

Length of leet about 7m (23ft) Other measurements similar to a round stack

POTATO PIT ((CLAMP))
BEING MADE

BALL POINTS ON ENDS OF TINES
TO PREVENT DAMAGE TO POTATOES

1·2m (4·FEET)

2·4m (8·FEET)

STABLE GRAIPS

1. MAN USING POTATO GRAIP (HARP) SHOVELLING (SHEELING) POTATOES OUT OF CART AND SHAPING THE PIT.

2. MAN WITH POTATO GRAIP HELPING TO SHAPE THE PIT.

3. MAN USING STABLE GRAIP BRINGING WHEAT BUNCHES TO END OF THE PIT, CART-LOAD OF BUNCHES WOULD BE ON ITS WAY TO THE PIT.

4. WOODEN BATTEN - MOVED ALONG EVERY SHIFT.

5. RIDGE OR POINT.

6. LAYER OF WHEAT STRAW 5 INCHES (12·5cm) THICK (COMPRESSED).

7. FIRST COVERING OF SOIL 3·INCHES (7·5cm) DEEP. RIDGE KEPT CLEAR TO ALLOW VENTILATION OF POTATOES WHILE SWEATING AND CURING TOOK PLACE, WHICH LASTED ABOUT 2 TO 3 WEEKS.

8. STEP TO HOLD MORE EARTHING UP.

9. FINAL EARTHING UP DONE IN TWO STAGES. SOME DUNG WAS SPREAD ON THE PITS IF SEVERE FROST WAS EXPECTED.

FOUNDATIONS MADE FOR SOME POTATO PITS WERE PLOUGHED OUT TO A DEPTH OF 5 OR 6 INCHES ON GRASS FIELDS DUE TO BE PLOUGHED LATER ON. THE FURROWS WERE SHOVELLED OUT AND SCATTER-ED ON EITHER SIDE.

RIDGE KEPT CLEAR OF SOIL. TO ACT AS VENT WHILE POTATOES ARE CURING.

SHOVELFULS OF SOIL TO KEEP THE STRAW IN PLACE TEMPORARILY.

PIT FACE

DOOR SHAPING SIDE OF PIT

PLAN OF PIT

WHEN SPREADING THE BUNCHES ON THE POTATOES ALONG THE SIDES OF THE PIT AFTER THE STRINGS ARE CUT SUFFICIENT OVERLAP BETWEEN EACH LOOSE BUNCH IS NECESSARY TO PREVENT LEAVING SEAMS BETWEEN EACH BUNCH WHICH WOULD ENCOURAGE FROST AND WATER TO SEEP INTO THE POTATO CROP. OVERLAPPING IS ALSO REQUIRED UP AND DOWN SIMILAR TO SLATES OR TILES ON A ROOF.

40

so he could leave what the rake had collected into rows of loose hay after the main crop of hay had been built into coles or rucks. The hay rakings were put into a stable loft to be fed to work horses.

CARTING OR HAULING COLES OR RUCKS TO A HAY-STACK

There were four different ways at least of getting hay to the haystacks being built in a stack-yard or in a field.

Coles or rucks loaded on to flat carts by a lifter that consisted of a triangular frame on wheels fitted with a belt and pulley system for lifting the coles or rucks using a horse. The hay was gripped from underneath by broad plates before lifting commenced. The same horse pulled the lifter to the next cole or ruck to be loaded. Special care had to be taken when working near low overhead wires.

By forking coles or rucks on to flat carts.

By using a horse drawn low set, flat bogie that was tilted by releasing a catch, then backed underneath part of the ruck (coles couldn't be loaded on to them) at the bottom. Two wire or sisal ropes were unwound from two windlasses on either side of the bogie at the front, and the ends of the ropes which were attached to large iron cleeks were pulled to the rear of the ruck where the cleeks were hooked together near the bottom of the ruck. Using a cranking handle, the ruck was wound up past the point of balance, locking the catch. It was now ready for the journey to the stack being built.

By dragging rucks(no tripods) with tractors or horses, using draught chains attached to ropes, similar to what were used on the hay bogies. This method was used only in fields where the stack was being built in the same field or a field close by.

BUILDING HAY-STACKS USING A HORSE-FORK

Haystacks were built by two men using pitchforks where hay was passed up to them by a horse fork that consisted of a tall stout wooden pole made up of two halves joined together, with a jib that could swing over the stack when the fork was loaded. The fork was attached to a thick rope that ran on pulleys on the jib, down the side of the pole, over another pulley, and finally hitched to a horse with draught chains. The horse led by a man, woman or boy walked forward to pull the forkful of hay up to the stack. The forkful of hay was then swung over above the stack where the two men on the stack with pitchforks, pushed it to where it was required. Once in position one of them would call to someone on the ground, to tug a rope attached to a trip on the fork. This released the hay and the horse was then backed, to allow the fork to be lowered, and loaded with more hay from the cole or ruck sited close to the stack being built.

The haystacks were either round or oblong shaped, thatched and ring roped.

ASSEMBLING THE HORSE-FORK

The horse fork pole that was about 45feet(13.5m) long, was lifted manually from the ground by the top or narrow end where a small ladder was placed underneath, before a longer ladder was then used to push the end of the pole further upwards, high enough for a guy rope to be hitched to a horse or tractor. The rope was pulled until the pole was in an upright position. Folk were steadying the pole with the other three guy ropes during the operation. The ropes were finally tied to metal pegs that were firmly hammered into the ground.

SHIFTING THE HORSE-FORK

Once the guy ropes were untied from their pegs and held by two men to a rope, a shovel, or a specially made plate that anchored the pole when in the working position, was inserted underneath the pole. The pole was then pulled from near the bottom by a horse or tractor while the guy ropes were slackened and tightened time about, until the new position of the pole was attained, whether to build another round stack or extend an oblong shaped stack. Finally the four guy ropes were tied to pegs that were well hammered into the ground.

THE GRAIN HARVEST

A binder that was used to cut and tie the crop into sheaves was pulled by two or three horses using draught chains and a long pole, that went up between two horses.

A swingle-tree with leather straps at the end of the pole enabled the straps to be tied to the collars of the horses.

When reaping it ran on two wheels, one a large broad ground-driven wheel with a sprocket wheel fixed to one side of the hub. The large wheel that was situated below the sheaf-making deck supplied the drive to the moving parts on the binder, by chains, sprockets and gear wheels. The smaller wheel shielded by a crop divider was fixed to the outer end of the platform. A broad canvas belt moved round long, narrow rollers, and received the crop cut by the cutter bar at the front of the binder. The crop was stroked backwards just below the heads of grain on to the canvas by six revolving flights bolted on to a conical shaped wheel at the end of a short shaft. The crop was then taken up between the upper and lower canvases, angled at about 45 degrees, on to the sheaf-making deck. When enough crop to be made into a sheaf, it weighed on a metal tongue or lever activating the tying system that consisted of a curved needle threaded with string from a twine box situated on the binder, a twine disc or retainer, that held the string tight, a knotter with a bill hook, and a small fixed knife. When the operation was completed a tied sheaf with a simple knot was pushed out from the deck by three or four strong tines attached to a shaft, turning a complete circle, anti-clockwise, looking from the rear of the binder. The sheaf normally landed with the long side up and the knot showing. The butt-end of the sheaf faced the direction the binder was travelling. A high seat was located at the rear of the binder to enable the horseman to drive his horses and operate the different handles as follows:

(1) - For lowering or raising the cutter bar.

(2) - For putting the flights up and down, and with the aid of a foot pedal, forwards and backwards.

(3) - For shifting the sheaf-making deck forward towards the wooden butter board, if the crop was short, or rearwards if the crop was tall. This ensured the string was tied at the middle of the sheaf. The butt or butter board moved with circular movements kept the ends of the straw stalks in line with the heads of grain while being packed into a sheaf by three or four curve shaped tines called packers which worked alternately with circular movements. The packers came up through separate slots

on the sheaf-making deck.

(4) - A handle that reached over the canopy above the sheaf- making deck to within reach of the horseman was used to pull a metal extension of the butter board rearwards, if the crop was very short.

(5) - A lever was provided for switching the drive from the large wheel, on or off.

The binder was raised or lowered by using the same cranking handle on each of the two wheels.

To transport the binder through gates etc., two transport wheels with half axles were used. The binder was raised as high as possible, and a transport wheel was inserted at the front of the binder and one at the rear, near the proximity of the large ground-driven wheel which was then wound up to its highest point. This was followed by lifting the outer-end of the platform, where the small wheel was situated and held there, until the pole with the swingle trees on it, was unhitched from the front of the binder, and inserted between two spokes of the small wheel. One end of the pole was then fixed to the underside of the platform. The small wheel was wound up tight, and clamped the pole. The binder was then ready to be hitched up to the horses again for transporting.

MAKING ROADS IN THE HARVEST FIELDS

Before any binders could go into a field of corn, a road was made by men cutting a swath of the crop round the edge of the field using scythes, followed by men and women tying the cut corn with bands made from the crop into sheaves. The sheaves were laid against the fence, dyke or hedge side to be stooked later on along with the ones made by the binders.

CUTTING AND STOOKING THE CORN

After a road was made in a field, the binders would commence to cut the crop round about until they finished up in the middle of the field. By this time a squad of folk working in pairs were stooking the sheaves. A person would pick up two sheaves, one by each hand, then holding them, one below each oxter, walked to a stook being made, or begin making another one, and let the sheaves, heads uppermost, slip from his or her arms, solidly, to make an inverted "V" shape, with the long sides of the sheaves facing outwards showing the knot tied on the string of each sheaf.

Stooks were mostly made up of ten sheaves, five on either side, appearing like small tents with open ends. This helped to encourage airflow through them so speeding up the drying and maturing of the crop.

The stooks remained in the fields for about three weeks. Stooks that had been blown over by strong winds had to be set up again, and in some cases stooks in a field that had been under-sown, were shifted on to fresh ground as the young grass sometimes withered under them.

BUILDING THE CORN CROP INTO STACKS

The horsemen driving the horses hitched to flat harvest carts would sometimes have orra-men with them to build the sheaves at the rear of the cart while they built the fore-end. Sheaves from two rows of stooks, a row on either of a cart moving from stook to stook, were passed up to them by folk using pitchforks. When the carts were loaded they were taken to the stack-yard at the farm, or to an end-rig near the gateway of the same field, where two rows of stacks were built with a road in between to allow a threshing mill to thresh the stacks from either side during the winter or a suitable time.

Stack builders were on their knees while building stacks, apart from when tying in the standing up sheaves at the very top of a stack.

THATCHING ROUND STACKS
(Diamond shaped roping)

After the building of the corn stacks was completed on a large farm, five or six thatchers with a server each, would commence to thatch the stacks. The thatchers were usually horsemen, tractormen and orra-men, while the servers were made up of orra-men, Irish harvestmen, haflins or loons, and women out-by workers.

A server's job was to keep the thatcher supplied with bunches of straw, rake up any "brockly" straw on the ground which had been swept off the thatch by the thatcher using a switch (a thin piece of straight, bare branch about three foot long).The server would have "spartie" (esparto grass rope) in balls or hanks, and a tappie made, ready for the roping down of the thatch.

The tappie that would sit at the top of the stack was made from five or six handfuls of clean stalks (stripped of their withered leaves) drawn individually from a bunch of wheat straw. The handfuls of stalks were then tightly tied together with binder twine, about six inches down from the threshed heads which were cut off neatly with a pair of sheep shears to give the tappie a thistle-like top.

The thatcher carried out his work standing on a ladder that made contact with easen or eaves only. The ladder was made secure by a graip pressed into the ground at the bottom of it, after the shaft had been threaded through between two rungs. The thatcher also used a graip partially stuck into the stack head halfway up the slope, to steady a bunch of wheat straw that was laid on its side against it, before the strings were cut.

He would commence thatching by taking a good handful of straw from the "loused" bunch and with the other hand lift the butt end of a sheaf belonging to a "gang", "coorse" or layer on the head, a good two feet up from the eaves, and lay the the threshed heads of the straw well underneath it, before releasing the sheaf, so clamping the straw. The thatcher would gradually work his way up and around the head, and shift the ladder accordingly.

When thatching was completed, the thatcher discarded a ring of chain that had acted as a collar holding the thatch in place at the peak of the stack. It was replaced by a piece of string tied tightly round the peaked thatch. The ladder was reset for roping to begin, and the thatcher climbed the ladder taking the hanks or balls of "spartie", tappie, and switch with him. When he had completed roping from one side of the head, he carried the ladder round to the opposite side of the stack and repeated the same procedure. The server on the ground would have been tying the rope ends into the respective sides of the stack about chest height at a focal point.

When roping was completed, diamond shapes appeared on the thatched head, made by the criss-crossing of the ropes. A thatched oat stack required at least eight ropes placed about 10 inches apart on opposite sides of the stack.

Narrower, thatched barley stacks needed fewer ropes than oat stacks. Large thatched wheat stacks built on stathels required the most ropes. Methods of thatching and roping varied between areas and counties.

THATCHING STACKS
(Ring roping)

Ring roping of a corn stack was done using rings of esparto rope placed no more than a foot apart, starting at the top of the stack and finishing at the eaves. As each rope was taken round the head, it was cinched at each of the six evenly spaced ropes that had been there since the stack was built. This type of roping was also used on oblong shaped corn stacks, and oblong and round hay-stacks.

THE POTATO HARVEST

The potato crop was gathered or picked by potato merchants' squads, Irish squads, town and city squads, farm folk, local folk and the older children on their two or three weeks holidays from school. Squads varied in numbers, thirty was a good manageable number. Each potato gatherer or picker was given the same length of stint or bit. It might be more or less than fifteen yards (13.65 metres) as lengths of bits varied, depending on the lengths of the drills and the number of potato pickers available. An able young laddie or lassie might be given a half bit to gather.

A potato digger pulled by two or three horses using a pole and draught chains, ran on two large ground driven wheels fitted with spade lugs that provided a positive drive to the machine. A coulter or sock cut underneath the drill, deep enough to prevent slicing the potatoes, and as the drill passed over it, the spinner wheel just behind it, fitted with curved tines, spun the drill to the side, exposing the potatoes ready for gathering into baskets. A screen was fitted to an extended arm on the digger to prevent the potatoes from being thrown too far out. A large lever was provided on the machine to lift the coulter out of the ground.

The horseman in charge of the digger usually walked up the drill next to the nearside digger wheel. A small wheel was fitted on the front of the heavier diggers that required three horses to pull them.

A horse and cart went up the drills behind the digger, only after the first five or six stints had been gathered into baskets. This allowed a cart to travel to the end of the drill without having to stop while the horseman was empting the baskets.

When the carts were loaded, they made their way to a potato clamp, often made on the end-rig of a stubble field. Three or four horse and carts would be involved in carting the potatoes.

Gathering potatoes behind the harrows was usually done by harrowing the ground where the potato crop was harvested that day. It was carried out just after "piece" time in the afternoon. The gatherers in pairs with a basket held between two folk, travelled across the field, in a reasonable straight line, and picked the potatoes that were being turned up by the harrows, and put them into the baskets. Two horse and carts were directly behind them to receive the filled baskets of potatoes.

POTATO CLAMP

Two or three men employed at the clamp helped the horsemen to empty their carts, shape the clamp and cover it with wheat straw and some soil. Afterwards the clamp was covered with extra soil to keep out the frost. A clamp was about four and half feet high to the ridge and approximately eight feet wide. The length of a clamp varied. It could be as long as eighty yards (72 metres) or more.

The cartloads of potatoes were backed in and tipped up at one side of the clamp. A door was set at an angle at the opposite side, propped up and made secure by graips, to contain the potatoes and shape that side of the clamp. When a section of the clamp was completed the door was slid along and made ready to extend the clamp with more potatoes. On some farms the loads were tipped up at the face, the end of the clamp, especially when tractors and trailers took the place of horses and carts.

SOWING WINTER WHEAT

Ploughing commenced as soon as the potato land was cleared of haulms, either by burning, carting off to a dump, or put into cattle courts. The corn drill or seeder pulled by two or three horses would start sowing after some land had been harrowed behind the ploughs. The land was sown up to where the ploughs had stopped at the end of the working day. Fresh ploughing and harrowing the next day provided a dry seed bed for seeding to commence right away. After the field was sown, it was then harrowed. Two or three corn drills might be used on a large arable farm.

SWEDES AND TURNIPS

In Scotland swedes and turnips were known together colloquially speaking as turnips. However there is a difference between the two.

The swede originated in Sweden and was first grown in Scotland around the 1770s. The green leaves are smooth in texture, and the bulb has white or cream coloured flesh with skins of purple, green or bronze hues. Being a good keeper it could be stored in clamps for as long as five months. The leaves grew up from a shank, unlike the yellow turnip, at the top of the bulb which offered a good hand grip for pulling it out off the ground, before topping and tailing it, that is cutting the haulm and roots off with a tapner, a curved knife with a hooked tip. Many countries in Europe grew swedes, especially in Holland and Germany.

The turnip or yellow turnip is a member of the mustard family. It originally came from Asia. The leaves are pale green, the bulb usually white fleshed and soft compared with the swede, and the skin is bronze coloured. They were never stored in clamps. Instead, with the haulms and roots kept on them, were fed to outside cattle or sheep. When singling the turnips in June, the young plants were sometimes mistaken for charlock plants as they too belong to the mustard family.

TOPPING AND TAILING SWEDES

Topping and tailing swedes for carting to turnip sheds or storing in clamps was done by putting four drills into one row. A squad of folk worked in pairs. Each pair of workers using tapners would top and tail two drills, one drill each, the length of the field, then return topping and tailing the other two drills, the swedes landing on top of the other ones already topped and tailed. Eventually there would be rows of swedes with roads in between to allow carts to be loaded by hand on both sides.

TURNIP CLAMP

On arable livestock farms where beef cattle were fed inside, the swedes were made into large, long clamps about six or seven feet high to the ridge or point. The swedes were fed to the cattle during the winter and early spring. A covering of wheat straw and earth kept the swedes free of frost. Storing of swedes was ideally completed by the November term. Clamps were opened up when the turnip sheds required refilling.

Many dairy farms required swedes stored in clamps, for them to be fed to milk cows, and young stock.

Farmers that produced calves and lambs required swedes to be fed to suckler cows whether inside cattle courts or outside in the fields, and ewes that had lambed in March were fed whole or sliced swedes until the grass became more plentiful.

SMALL CLAMPS OF SWEDES

Small clamps were made in the turnip field. They were made from six cartloads of swedes, a load-length of about seventy yards (63m) between each clamp, and a distance of about thirty yards (27m) between each row. They were covered with wheat straw and earth to keep out the frost.

Throughout the winter and spring the swedes from the clamps were sliced or chipped by a mechanical turnip cutter, and put into large deep troughs for the hoggets as part of their feed along with hay and a corn mix. The hay was put into hecks that sat on four wheels, and the corn mix or concentrates was put into shallow troughs. The clamps were netted off, allowing the sheep to run on the cleared part of the field. When a clamp was used up, the turnip cutter and feed troughs were moved to the next clamp. Some turnip cutters were self-propelled.

SHEUCHIN' SWEDES

Sheuchin' swedes was done by using a plough to make sheuchs or trenches to take two drills of swedes which were pulled by hand and laid in them, with the haulms uppermost. They were then covered with soil using a plough. Sheuchin' swedes commenced at one side of the field, and progressed across to the other side, filling the sheuchs with swedes as they were being made. The swedes were ploughed up, in late spring and topped and tailed. Only two drills were put into one row this time. The swedes were then carted off the field to be fed to cattle or sheep.

OTHER CROPS THAT MIGHT HAVE BEEN GROWN ON SOME FARMS

Mashlam.- consisted of beans and oats, used either as silage, or built into stacks and threshed later on. The oats and beans were gristed into meal and fed to dairy cows.

Beans - stacked to be threshed later on. They were gristed into meal and used in feed mixes to be fed to cattle. Beans were also grown for seed and sold to grain merchants.

Flax - was grown on some farms during the time of the war in the 1940s. It was made into linen, oil and linseed cake. The cake was fed to cattle.

Mangolds- they were similar in shape to a carrot but much larger. The haulms were cut off, but the roots were kept on. They were stored in clamps, to be fed to cattle or sheep in the Spring.

Fodder beet - similar in shape to mangolds. The roots were left on them, but the haulms were cut off. They were stored in clamps, and fed to cattle later on.

Sugar beet - looked like fodder beet. The haulms were cut off, but the roots were left on them. They were stored in temporary clamps before being taken to the sugar beet factory by rail and road. The sugar beet was finally made into sugar and a by product beet pulp was fed to livestock.

During the second war, farmers who hadn't grown sugar beet before the war were encouraged by the government to grow the crop.

Kale - made up of large thick stems with plenty of leaves, was fed mainly to dairy cows. Daily rations were cut and carted off to the farm if the cows were housed. Some farms strip grazed the kale.

Rape - not unlike kale, a bit smaller, was grown for fattening sheep, or for going on to fatten them on swedes.

Cabbages - young plants were transplanted from trays on to drill tops or ridges. The mature cabbages were fed to young tups or calves.

RIG-MARKING A FIELD USING A LONG MARKER

Rig marking stubble fields to be dunged, was done using a drill plough pulled by a pair of horses. It was set to make shallow ruts five yards (4.5m) apart measured by a long marker that made a mark on the ground for the horseman to use as a guide to make the ruts straight. It was fixed to a hinge on the drill plough, and was swung round at each end of the field for the return journey.

CARTING DUNG TO A FIELD FROM THE MIDDEN

After a field was rig marked, carts were loaded with dung from the midden by using graips. Once a cart was loaded it was taken to a field and set in the middle of a rig. A man at the rear of the cart using a muck hack, made a small heap of dung every five yards. He called to the horseman when he wanted the cart stopped or when to move on. A trace horse was used to help pull the cart if there were steep slopes in the field or slippery ground conditions.

SPREADING THE DUNG HEAPS IN THE FIELDS

As the dung was being carted from the midden and made into heaps, some of the orra-squad including the women and maybe a loon would be spreading the heaps. A heap spread evenly covered an area of five square yards or 4.5m squared.

PLOUGHING

Ploughing would commence after all the dung was carted out. The orra-men who filled the carts and emptied them, joined the squad already spreading the heaps of dung. Ploughing would continue throughout the winter and spring. There were always old grass fields to plough for growing oats or potatoes, clean stubble fields, no dung spread on them, and red land, land cleared of potatoes or turnips.

Ploughing ceased when severe frost made the ground too hard to plough. If severe frost did take hold, cattle courts could be mucked out

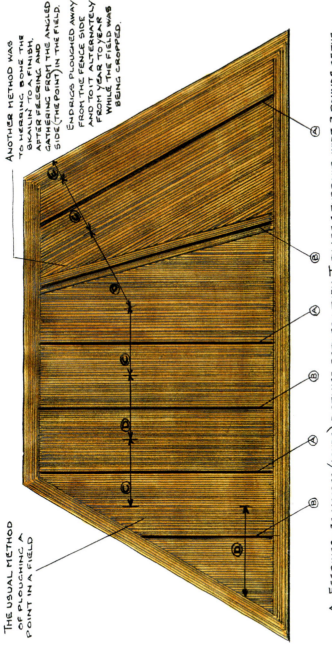

HORSE PLOUGHING
WITH A SINGLE FURROW PLOUGH

THE USUAL METHOD OF PLOUGHING A POINT IN A FIELD

ANOTHER METHOD WAS TO HERRING BONE THE SKAILIN' TO A FINISH. AFTER FEERING AND GATHERING FROM THE ANGLED SIDE (THE POINT) IN THE FIELD.

ENDRIGS PLOUGHED AWAY FROM THE FENCE SIDE AND TO IT ALTERNATELY FROM YEAR TO YEAR WHILE THE FIELD WAS BEING CROPPED.

A - FEERINGS - 36 METRES (40YDS) DISTANCE BETWEEN THEM. THEY ARE 6 FURROWS WIDE. 3 ROUNDS OF THE PLOUGH. BY THIS TIME THE PLOUGHMAN HAS ATTAINED THE REQUIRED DEPTH NEEDED FOR A SPECIFIC CROP TO BE GROWN.

B - FINISHES - 36 METRES (40YDS) DISTANCE BETWEEN THEM.

C - GETHERING - 18 METRES (20YDS) WIDE. PLOUGHED CLOCKWISE.

D - SKAILING - 18 METRES (20YDS) WIDE. PLOUGHED ANTI-CLOCKWISE.

E - ENDRIGS - 4.5 METRES (5YDS) WIDE. USED FOR TURNING ON. PLOUGHED LAST.

ALL MEASUREMENTS VARIABLE.

THRESHING GRAIN STACKS

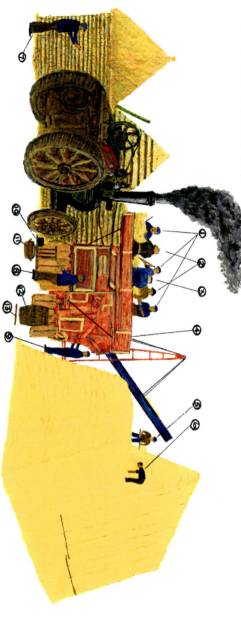

1. THREE FORKERS USED ON TWO GRAIN STACKS. TWO OF THEM FORKED ONE SHEAF AT A TIME TO A LOUSER EACH.
2. TWO WOMEN LOUSERS WHO CUT THE STRINGS ON THE SHEAVES AND PASSED ONE TIME ABOUT TO THE MILL-MAN.
3. THE MILL-MAN FED THE LOUSED SHEAVES DOWN A SLOT TO BE TAKEN IN BETWEEN THE ROTATING DRUM AND THE CONCAVE.
4. TWO FORKERS UNSEEN.-ONE FORKED THE BUNCHES FROM THE MILL TO THE MAN PUTTING THEM ON THE ELEVATOR.
5. MAN PASSING THE BUNCHES TO THE BUILDER OF THE STACK OR SOO.
6. THE SOO BUILDER WAS USUALLY THE FOREMAN.

NOTE.- A WOMAN WOULD BE EMPLOYED TO CARRY THE CHAFF AWAY FROM THE MILL USING A SHEET, IF A CHAFF BLAST WASN'T FITTED TO THE THRESHING MILL.

7. MAN TAKING ROPES OFF STACK BEFORE STRIPPING THE THATCH OFF. HE WOULD ALSO BE GIVING THE MAN ON THE GRAIN A HAND.
8. MAN WEIGHING AND TYING SACKS OF GRAIN TO BE LIFTED BY HORSE AND CART OR TRACTOR AND TRAILER.
9. THE FIRST MILL-MAN.
10. WEIGHS, WITH 56LBWTS PLUS AN EMPTY SACK AS COUNTER BALANCE.
11. BUSHEL MEASURE WITH GRAIN AND SCOOP USED WHEN WEIGHING SACKS OF GRAIN.
12. BARREL FOR SETTING SACK OF GRAIN ON BEFORE A MAN PUTS IT ON HIS BACK AND CARRIES IT TO THE GRANARY E.G.
13. STICK USED BETWEEN TWO MEN TO LIFT THE SACK OF GRAIN ON TO THE BARREL OR A CART, TRAILER OR LORRY.
14. THE SACK OF GRAIN WAS PULLED BACK OVER THE STICK NEAR THE BOTTOM AND WAS CRADLED READY FOR LIFTING UP.

Straw Soo

Name given to a stack of threshed straw bunches tied by the threshing mill whilst threshing grain stacks

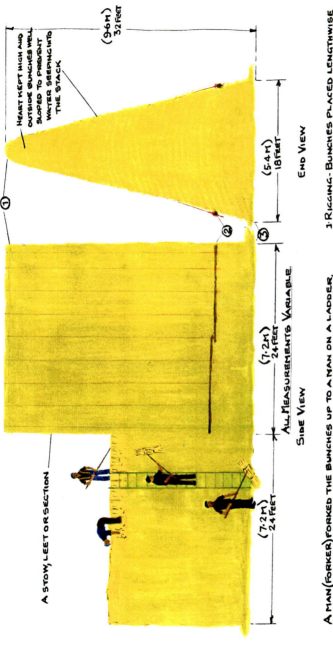

Heart kept high and outside bunches well sloped to prevent water seeping into the stack

(9.6m) 32 Feet

(5.4m) 18 Feet

End View

A stow, leet or section

(7.2m) 24 Feet

All Measurements Variable.

Side View

(7.2m) 24 Feet

① ② ③

1. Rigging - Bunches placed lengthwise.
2. Esparto grass rope tied to props.
3. Foundation - Loose straw.

A man (forker) forked the bunches up to a man on a ladder, who passed (crawed) the bunches up to a man who forked them over to the builder. When eventually elevators were used the forkers job on the stack was called crawin'.

Sometimes a cart was put along-side the stack empty or with bunches on it to act as a gantry.

55

POTATO DRESSER
SHOWN WITHOUT PULLEYS AND ENDLESS BELTS

WARE RIDDLE
SEED RIDDLE

ENGINE

ARMS FOR SUSPENDING
RECIPROCATING BOX WHICH
HELD THE RIDDLES IN PLACE

INTAKE ELEVATOR

SMALL HOPPER

CHATS, SMALL STONES AND CHIRLES.

CROSS SECTION
TO ALLOW TRAVEL OF POTATOES TO BE SEEN

PICKING ELEVATOR
WARE

SEED

PLAN

HANDLES FOR
FLIPPING OVER
FLAPS TO ALLOW
THE SACKS TO BE
FILLED TIME ABOUT.

CLOSELY SPACED RODS WHICH ALLOWED
SOIL ONLY TO FALL THROUGH BETWEEN THEM.

NOTE - SLOW TURNING ROLLERS
FIXED ACROSS THE WIDTH
OF THE PICKING ELEVATOR
BECAME POPULAR AROUND
THE 1950's. THIS ENABLED THE
PICKERS TO SPOT DAMAGED OR
DISEASED POTATOES MORE EASILY.

56

A VARIETY OF EQUIPMENT
USED ON FARMS

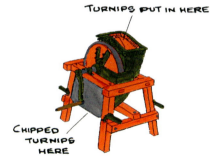

TURNIPS PUT IN HERE

CHIPPED TURNIPS HERE

TURNIP CUTTER

TURNIPS PUT IN HERE

SLICED TURNIPS HERE

TURNIP SLICER

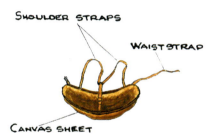

SHOULDER STRAPS

WAIST STRAP

CANVAS SHEET

SOWING SHEET

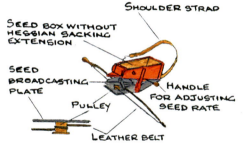

SHOULDER STRAP

SEED BOX WITHOUT HESSIAN SACKING EXTENSION

SEED BROADCASTING PLATE

PULLEY

HANDLE FOR ADJUSTING SEED RATE

LEATHER BELT

"FIDDLE BOW" ACTION SEEDER

GRAIN PAN

USED FOR FILLING SACKS WITH GRAIN FROM A HEAP ON THE GRANARY FLOOR.

HAND BARROW

USED WHEN MUCKING OUT THE STABLE. THE DUNG WAS CARRIED ON IT AND TAKEN INTO THE "STABLE" REED TO BE DUMPED AND SPREAD.

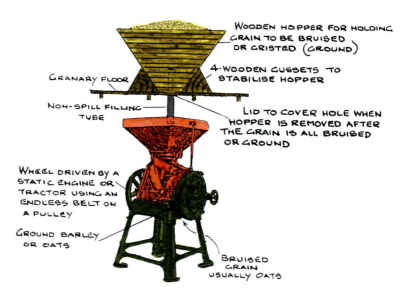

Wooden hopper for holding grain to be bruised or gristed (ground)

4·wooden gussets to stabilise hopper

Granary floor

Non-spill filling tube

Lid to cover hole when hopper is removed after the grain is all bruised or ground

Wheel driven by a static engine or tractor using an endless belt on a pulley

Ground barley or oats

Bruised grain usually oats

Corn bruiser and grinder

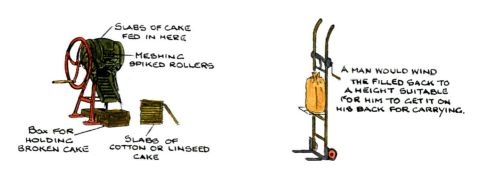

Slabs of cake fed in here

Meshing spiked rollers

Box for holding broken cake

Slabs of cotton or linseed cake

A man would wind the filled sack to a height suitable for him to get it on his back for carrying.

Cake mill or breaker

Sack lifter

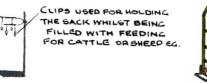

Clips used for holding the sack whilst being filled with feeding for cattle or sheep eg.

Sack holder

Sack barrow

Tools which would be used throughout the year

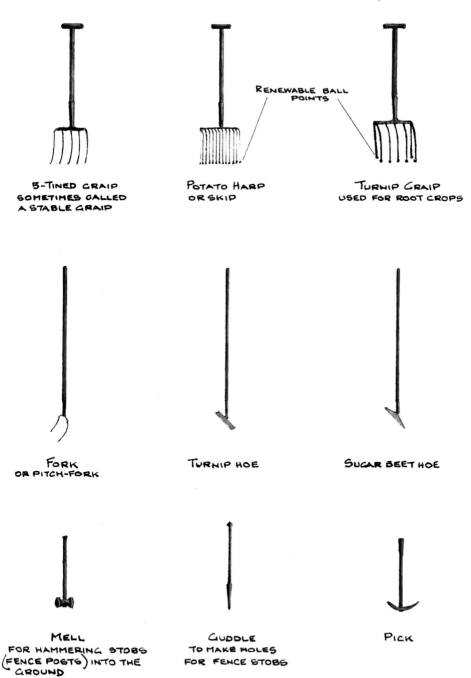

5-Tined Graip
Sometimes called
a Stable Graip

Potato Harp
or Skip

Renewable ball
points

Turnip Graip
used for root crops

Fork
or Pitch-fork

Turnip hoe

Sugar Beet hoe

Mell
for hammering stobs
(fence posts) into the
ground

Guddle
to make holes
for fence stobs

Pick

Spade
Used when making
field drains

Shovel

Muck Hawk

Spade

Graip with close spaced tines
Used for digging and shovelling
small stones etc.

Hedge Bill

Scythe

Tapner

Sugar beet knife
Used for cutting shaws off
the beet after it had been pulled
out off the ground and laid into rows.

**Replacable
wooden teeth**

Wooden rake

60

and the dung made into heaps in a field or made into a midden. Threshing corn stacks could also be done in the frosty weather.

Before a field was ploughed, the end-rig that was used for turning on was marked with a shallow furrow about five yards from the fence, hedge or dyke side using feering poles or suitable markers as a guide. This let the horsemen know when to enter and exit the plough at each end of the field.

Feerings were drawn straight by using red and white striped poles or suitable markers set up in a straight line. Feerings were about forty yards (36m) apart for horse ploughing using a single furrow plough. They were six furrows wide as by this time the ploughman was expected to be ploughing the required depth for a specific crop to be grown. The first two furrows were ploughed against each other when ploughing lea for growing a crop of oats. On clean stubble or red-land, the first two furrows were ploughed outwards then ploughed back in again, although some horsemen ploughed the first two furrows together.

In fields where potatoes and turnips were to be grown, two or three furrows were ploughed out then ploughed back in again. This ensured that the feering furrows were deep enough to be tilled to the same depth as the rest of the field during the spring cultivations. Fields to be growing a potato or turnip crop were either leys or dunged stubble fields.

Gathering was ploughing a twenty yards (18m) wide rig in a clockwise direction around a feering.

Skailin was ploughing a twenty yards (18m) wide rig between two gatherings in an anti-clockwise direction.

Finish or Hintin was the trench left in the middle after the skailin was completed.

Scour or Mould furrow was the last furrow to be ploughed in the finish. It was made up of clean soil, no grass or trash, and wasn't as wide or as high as the other furrows.

Skin and trenching was done on leys where a potato or turnip crop was to be grown. One plough skinned the grass from the top of the furrow to be ploughed, into the bottom of the last ploughed furrow, while another plough following behind, buried the grass by ploughing a furrow on top of it.

Steering the soil was done by ploughing a field crosswise in the

Spring- time that had already been ploughed in the backend of the previous year. It was usually done on fields where a turnip crop was to be grown.

Horse ploughing can be seen at some of the ploughing matches or competitions and farming yester-year shows, held throughout the country at different times of the year.

MAINTENANCE WORK CARRIED OUT THROUGHOUT THE YEAR

Cutting thistles and nettles etc. around the farm, in grazing fields, and the edges of cornfields before the corn was ripe.

Topping seeded grazing fields using a mower.

Trimming or cutting hedges with a billhook.

Cleaning out ditches and repairing damaged field drains.

Repairing fences and dykes during the grazing season to ensure livestock were secured safely.

A SAMPLE OF MAINTENANCE DONE ON SOME MACHINES AND IMPLEMENTS

Ploughs were remounted, that is worn parts were replaced on shares, coulter points and wings. Blade coulters laid by the local blacksmith by hammering hot metal on to the worn cutting edges of the coulters. Mould boards were cleaned and smeared with grease or waste oil.

Harrows were checked for worn and slack tines that often required a blacksmith to carry out the necessary repairs.

Drill ploughs had the detachable worn socks or points laid by the blacksmith.

Tumbling Tams, or Hay-sweeps. Broken or cracked wooden tines replaced by the local joiner or cartwright.

The Binder was given a good service before harvest time was due.

Canvases that had been repaired by a saddler in a nearby town were fitted on to the binder.

The knife made up of a row of small triangular cutting sections were checked for cracks or wear and were replaced if necessary.

Fingers on the knife bar were also checked for wear or breaks. Spars were replaced on the wooden flights if broken or split.

Grease was applied to grease nipples, and moving parts inside sleeves or tubes were greased or oiled.

Binder twine from the twine box was threaded through the needle with the end of the string held tightly in the retainer and the knotter checked out, to ensure it was tying properly.

The Potato digger had the spade-lugs on the ground driven wheels checked and replaced or tightened up if slack. The coulter or sock replaced if too badly worn and hessian sacking replaced on the screen. Finally grease holders with caps that could be screwed down as the grease was being used up by the rotating shafts were filled with grease. Grease nipples on the digger were greased. The oil in the gearbox was checked and replenished if required.

Implements and machines should have been cleaned and treated with a preservative such as waste oil or grease at sometime. Lubricating moving parts on a machine at one time was done by pouring oil into a small hole with or without a piece of jute waste or something similar. After the material was well soaked a small lid was flipped down to seal the hole. Some oil holes just took the lubricant directly to the rotating shaft inside the casing.

All cart axle ends were greased throughout the year at sometime. The horses appreciated smooth turning wheels when pulling the carts.

The large wooden cart-wheels fitted with iron tyres were replaced by smaller wheels with rubber tyres on farm carts by the 1950s. And speaking of horses, they were taken to the smithy to have worn, lost or slack shoes replaced.

SOME TASKS MOSTLY DONE DURING THE WINTER MONTHS

On wet days or during a spell of incessant snowing, horsemen would have a spell of cleaning and polishing harness, after dismantling it into various pieces. Some horsemen had their own bits of harness and decorations whilst other lads had a complete set of harness with decorations for showing at agricultural shows or ploughing matches.

Some horses were exercised if snow prevented them from being used for work although this was rare. A horse would be exercised using a lunge rein. The horseman stood in the same spot while the horse circled around him, either walking or cantering.

Horses while stabled were clipped of hair that usually took in the bellies to halfway up their sides and the topmost parts of their legs, leaving the harness to sit on the undipped hair.

Clipping was also carried out on the housed cattle in the reeds or cattle courts, using the horse clippers. The cattle were lassoed using a thick rope. They were then made secure beside a wooden or steel upright (stanchion) in the reed. The head was usually clipped first then a strip about four inches wide was clipped along the back to the tail head then down to the beginning of the switch. This helped to cool them a bit, and also made them suitable for selling at a livestock mart. As a final bit of grooming the switch was given a trim then combed using a horse's manes and tails comb.

Cattle crates for restraining cattle didn't arrive on farms until the early 1950s.

Assisting with testing cattle for Brucellosis, for instance.

Filling up the corn chests in the stable with bruised or rolled oats.

Putting slabs of cotton or linseed cake through a cake breaker that was put into motion by turning a cranking handle. The broken cake was fed to livestock.

Sorting out empty hessian sacks that had held potatoes, fertiliser, grain and feed stuffs etc. The whole ones were bundled into lots of twenty and tied tightly with string

Torn or rotted hessian sacks were bundled up, ready for a scrap merchant to collect.

Discarding rotted spartie (esparto grass rope) before rolling the good rope into balls or hanks.

Esparto rope was dumped temporarily in a shed, after being taken off thatched stacks or hay rucks.

Burning chaff, left by a contractors threshing mill.

Cleaning and tidying up sheds around the farm, and doing some maintenance work on the inside threshing mill.

THRESHING CORN STACKS

Threshing corn stacks was done by a threshing mill, and a traction steam engine belonging to a contractor. The threshing mill was driven by an endless belt on the flywheel of the engine and a pulley on the threshing mill. Often the mill was set between two rows of stacks to be threshed in a field near a gateway or set in the stack-yard.

Sometimes loads of sheaves from stacks were drawn along side the mill to be threshed.

Sheaves were forked by two men from stacks or a load of sheaves, to two women "lousers" on top of the mill, a forker to each louser. The women cut the strings on the sheaves, and passed a sheaf, time about to the mill-man who fed the "loused" sheaves down a slot to be taken in between a fast rotating drum with rasp bars and a concave, a curved thick piece of metal with spaces wide enough for the threshed grain to fall into the grain pan then on to sieves and riddles, up an elevator then on to finish up in sacks after being screened for grain size by a rotary screen.

The firsts or good grain came out of two chutes, the seconds or smaller grains came out of one chute, and the thirds or lights came out of two chutes.

The chaff separated from the grain by a fan blowing air from underneath the sieves fell on the ground, and was raked on to a large chaff sheet which was bundled up and taken to a cattle court for bedding the cattle, or dumped in a handy place to be burned later on. Eventually, chaff- blasts that blew the chaff along detachable pipes to a suitable place were fitted to threshing mills.

The straw was shunted along on wooden straw-walkers inside the threshing mill to be tied into bunches that were built into a large stack.

The sacks that were made secure by hooks while being filled with the best grain, were weighed as follows - Oats 1.5cwt. (75kgs), Barley 1.5cwt-2cwt. (l00kgs), Wheat 2cwt.-2.25cwt (112.5kgs) and beans 2.5cwt (125kgs).

If grain was dumped loose on the floor of the granary loft, the sacks were filled up as catch weights.

The farmer whose corn stacks was threshed by a contractor, supplied coal for the traction steam engine, and meals for the two mill men. He also provided dinner and tea breaks for the men and women working at the threshing mill.

Large tractors were replacing the traction steam engines around the 1940s, and the threshing mills became less apparent by the 1970s, and can only be seen nowadays at vintage machinery shows along with traction steam engines, tractors and implements etc.

INSIDE THRESHING MILLS

Many farms had a stationary threshing mill situated below the granary loft and close to feed and straw barns. The different ways of driving the mill varied over the years as follows, in chronological order.

Horses hitched to the ends of bars on a horizontal wheel, similar to a capstan on a ship, walked round in a circle, and turned a bevelled gear. on a shaft which went through a hole in the wall to the threshing mill.

A stationary engine using an endless belt on its pulley and a pulley on the mill.

A tractor using an endless belt on its pulley and a pulley on the mill.

The gearing house which had a dome shaped roof where the horses walked round was called a mill ring or a mill gang. These buildings can be seen on some farms today. The inside mills were used mainly for threshing oat stacks, to have a supply of bruised oats for feeding to horses, cattle and sheep. The straw was used for bedding and feed.

Most of those threshing mills were dismantled and scrapped during the 1950s and the 1960s.

DRESSING OR GRADING OF POTATOES

Potato dressing was done by a potato dresser driven by a small petrol engine fixed to a frame on top of the dresser, using an endless belt on the pulley of the engine and a large wheel on the dresser. The dresser that sat on four small iron wheels was set in at the clamp face after enough soil and straw had been stripped off the clamp to allow potato dressing to commence.

Potatoes were shovelled on to an elevator which took the potatoes upwards to fall on to an oblong shaped, square meshed riddle, fixed to a reciprocating box which shunted the potatoes back and forth until some of the potatoes fell through the squares of the riddle, on to another riddle beneath it with smaller squares. Potatoes that fell through it went down a small chute into a basket at ground level, were called chats that were no more than an inch in diameter. The potatoes that remained on the top riddle were classed as ware, or in some cases tops, when using a riddle with much larger squares, and the potatoes that remained on the riddle below it were known as seed potatoes.

The ware and seed potatoes travelled along their respective riddles on to an elevator, with a partition that kept them apart, and then into sacks held by quick releasing hooks. When filled they were unhooked and weighed as 1cwt sacks of ware or seed. The sacks were stitched or sewn by using twine and a large curved needle.

The ware was sold for boiling, baking, chips and processing.

The seed was sold to potato growers in the United Kingdom and abroad.

The chats were either dumped or fed to livestock.

The brock that included diseased, damaged, green and misshaped potatoes etc. was sometimes fed to livestock.

A potato dressing squad made up of men and women would require one man to shovel the potatoes on to the first elevator. Three women and the gaffer of the squad, would pick off the brock potatoes, stones, and pieces of haulms from the ware and seed potatoes. Two men and a woman might be needed on the weighing and tying of the sacks,

At the end of the day straw was put back on to the uncovered part of the clamp and on the sacks of potatoes, although quite often the sacks of potatoes, both ware and seed, were carted to the nearby railway station to be put into wagons, or vans to be transported to their destinations while dressing continued at the potato clamp. Potato dressing was mostly done by potato merchants and Irish squads.

MAN-POWERED POTATO DRESSERS AND HAND RIDDLES

Before potato dressers had engine power, smaller versions were made that were put into motion by one or two men turning a large wheel with a cranking handle.

Dressing of potatoes before machines were available was done by using hand riddles with different sized squares ringed with wicker sides that were about four inches (9.8cms) deep and about two and half feet (73.5cms) in diameter. They were held in front of the body at waist height, and potatoes that were put into them were shaken up and down and back and forth, until the desired dressing of the potatoes was attained. By this time the brock had been picked off the riddles. And the potatoes on the riddles were emptied into seed or ware hoppers respectively, which held the sacks to be filled, weighed and sewn.

SOWING SHEET

A sowing sheet was made up of a canvas tray with six inch deep wicker sides and straps enabling it to be fastened over the shoulders and at the waist in front of a person. Sowing was done by dipping the hands time about into the tray, and filling them with either seeds or fertiliser. The arms were swung backwards and forwards alternately releasing material from the hands at the same time. A good regular stride and the correct distance between each pass were essential for the right rate of application.

THRAWCRUICK

An apparatus used for making straw ropes. Straw was pulled and twisted by hand from a heap of loose straw, and after some length was achieved, the infant ropes were fixed to three or four hooks which were rotated by a gearing driven by a crank handle turned by a man harnessed to the thrawcruick. He stepped back slowly while turning the handle. This kept the ropes taut and prevented them from getting too thick. Assistance was required for this job. Straw ropes were used for keeping thatch in place on stacks, and making hay rucks secure.

HORSES TO TRACTORS

As horses had to take enforced retirement from the farms by tractors becoming more available to farmers in the 1950s and the 1960s, many of the horse-drawn implements and machines were altered to enable them to be hitched to tractors. Poles were fitted to carts and machines to replace the horse shafts.

Some machines were fitted with a tripod frame so they could be hitched to a tractor with a top link and two arms that were operated by an oil pump built into the tractor.

It said much for the strength and design of those horse-drawn implements and machines, and not forgetting the carts which were loaded to excess at times, to have withstood the extra power and speed of the tractors. It didn't make much difference to the number of staff required on farms as horsemen became tractor-men. However, it did later on as more modern tractors with up to date implements, machines and trailers arrived on the farms.

Tractors with iron wheels had been used on some farms since 1918 doing jobs like ploughing with a trailing plough, harrowing, discing, pulling binders, mowers and driving threshing mills etc.

HOEING TO SPRAYING

Spraying for weed control among cereal crops was being done on some farms in Scotland around the early 1950s. Only certain parts of fields were sprayed at first. Eventually whole scale spraying of weed killers, pesticides and fungicides etc. was being carried out on most farms by the 1970s. This put an end to the weeding of turnip and potato crops.

LOOSE HAY TO BALED HAY

When balers with pick-up reels which made small oblong shaped bales became more acquirable for farmers in the 1950s, they were used at first to bale hay from coles or rucks built in the fields, and with some apprehension were used to bale the hay directly from swaths, after much turning and tedding of the crop. Eventually this became the normal practice on farms.

When baling of hay did take place, the bales of hay were carted home to the farm, and built temporarily in cattle courts or sheds, to remain no less than a week before being built in hay barns or sheds permanently as the hay in the bales would have cooled down by this time. Some farmers preferred to leave the bales, built up into blocks of eight or ten bales, in the fields for about two weeks. A lot depended on the condition of the hay before it was baled.

BINDERS TO COMBINE HARVESTERS

Combine harvesters were first used in Scotland on some large arable farms in the early 1950s. Some oats were combined at the beginning, but barley was the first crop to be combined completely and wheat was last to be combined as straw was still required for potato pits and thatch for stacks. However during the period between the early 1950s and the late 1960s the use of binders was phased out completely on most farms.

POTATO DIGGERS TO POTATO HARVESTERS

Potato harvesters appeared on many large arable farms in Scotland during the 1960s, after a rather tentative start in the early 1950s. Potato squads were still being used extensively at this time. However as improved potato harvesters were lifting more potatoes per day and showing a good clean sample of the crop, squads were steadily becoming redundant. Potato harvesters replaced the diggers and squads on most farms by 1970s.

POTATO CLAMPS TO POTATO STORES

On large arable farms in Scotland, making potato clamps came to an end in the 1960s. Existing sheds were made suitable for storing loose potatoes, and wheat straw was used for covering the crop to prevent chilling and greening. Eventually potatoes were stored in 10cwt.(500kg) boxes and finally in one tonne (1000kg) boxes in darkened, temperature controlled potato stores.

TOPPING AND TAILING OF TURNIPS BY HAND TO TURNIP HARVESTERS

In the 1950s topping and tailing turnip machines were being used on a few farms. The machines topped and tailed the turnips, and put two drills into one row, ready for loading by hand into trailers to be carted off to a clamp. However their stay was short lived as machines fitted with elevators arrived on the scene that loaded the turnips into trailers pulled by tractors travelling along side them.

CORN STACKS TO GRAIN DRYERS

Before grain dryers made their appearances on farms in Scotland, all the wheat, barley and oat crops etc. were built into stacks. Provided the sheaves were in good fettle, rustled when handled, no rawness inside the sheaves at the string, built correctly, that is, well hearted with plenty of slope given to the sheaves, thatched properly and roped down tightly. Stacks would yield good hard grain and clean dry straw when threshed.

As grain dryers were being built into existing buildings or new buildings, the art of building stacks and thatching them become obsolete by the 1960s on most farms.

GRAIPS TO DUNG LOADERS

Mucking out cattle courts and loading carts or trailers from dung middens using graips, was being taken over by mechanical loaders during the 1950s on some farms. The loaders were fitted on to tractors at the front, although some were rear-mounted. Soon most farms had a dung loader that could be hitched or unhitched in a matter of minutes.

MILK PRODUCTION

Dairy farms of varying sizes were found in cities, towns and villages in Scotland during the nineteenth century and part of the twentieth century. Some had ten cows or less whilst the large farms had fifty or more cows. Most of the large farms had grass parks, but the smaller ones used communal grass fields for summer grazing.

The owners of the dairies used horse-drawn milk carts (milk-floats) or handcarts to retail their milk to the local people. The housewifes came out with their milk jugs when they heard the milkman calling on them.

Dairy farmers from outlying districts retailed their milk to housewives, big houses, hospitals, and hotels etc. in the ever-growing cities and towns whilst other farmers sold their milk in returnable large metal cans to co-operative and private creameries, where the milk was retailed or made into cream, butter or cheese.

The two sizes of large cans used by farmers held ten gallons (45.5 litres) and eight gallons (36.5 litres) respectfully.

The names of the farms that supplied the milk were die stamped on them.

Much smaller cans were called flagons or pitchers.

A BOWMAN

Up until the 1920s, a dairyman or bowman in Scotland could manage a herd of dairy cows let to him at so many pounds sterling per cow by a farmer who might own or rent two or three farms in the same district. The bowman would manage the herd of cows assisted by his wife and the older siblings in the family, and retail the milk using his own horses and milk carts. The monies received from the sales of the milk, cream, butter and cheeses etc., were his income.

The farmer contracted to keep up the stock of cows and supply the natural feeding-stuffs and a quantity of artificial feed. The bowman who wished to do his cows even better purchased extra feed for them.

This method of dairying was called Bowing. In some cases a bowman might own the cows. A different contract would have to be formulated between him and the farmer.

HAND MILKERS

Hand milkers were usually made up of farmers, farmers' wives, maids, ploughmen and their wives, farmers' sons and daughters. Young lads and lassies could become proficient hand milkers before school leaving age.

Cows were milked twice a day, the first milking as early as 3 am and the second milking was done about 3 pm. All milk was refrigerated by a water-cooling system, before finishing up in large milk cans.

Hand milking of a cow was carried out by sitting on a stool with a luggie which had a capacity of about three gallons (13.5 litres), held between the knees. The milker sat close into the cow with their head resting lightly on the cow's flank. The cow's udder and teats were washed and dried before milking commenced.

There were many hand milking competitions held throughout Scotland.

HAND MILKING TO MACHINE MILKING

Hand milking gave way to machine milking using the bucket, or unit system on most farms in Scotland during the 1940s. The buckets that held about five gallons (22.75 litres) of milk and were designed to take a detachable lid that had a cluster of four tubes with a rubber lined teat cup fixed on one end of each tube. A long hose-pipe, also on the lid, could be connected to any one of the points along the metal airline pipe situated above the cow stalls. The airline was supplied by air from a vacuum pump powered by a petrol engine or an electric motor situated in a shed next to the byre. A pulsator, a small box fitted on the detachable lid, regulated the milking rhythm required to encourage the cow to let her milk down comfortably and as naturally as possible.

When a cluster was unhooked from the detachable lid on a bucket it could reach underneath a cow, so enabling the four teat cups to be slipped on to the teats for milking to commence, after the cow's udder and teats had been washed and dried. The bucket was placed in a safe position in the stall to prevent the cow from knocking it over with a foot.

During the milking period, the milk from the filled buckets was emptied into pails and taken to the dairy house where it was put through a water-cooled refrigeration unit before going into large milk cans. A bucket or unit could hold milk from two or three cows although this depended on the milk yields of the cows being milked at the time.

ROUND THE SHED SYSTEM

This system was introduced around the late 1950s. A pipe that went round the byre close to the airline pipe, carried the milk direct from a cow once she was milked, to the bulk tank where it was kept at a proper temperature. This system was short-lived as it was carried over to the milking parlours when they became popular, making the byres obsolete for dairying purposes.

MILKING PARLOURS

Milking parlours became popular in the 1960s, although some had been installed on farms before that. The herring-bone parlour is the most popular at the moment.

Cows in the collecting area of the dairy unit walk into stalls set at an angle, herring-bone pattern, on either side of a low-level pit or well, where the dairyman gives them their ration of special cake or pellets to sustain or improve their milk yields.

Cows udders and teats are washed and dried before milking commences. Each stall has a calibrated glass jar that measures a cow's milking yield whilst being milked. Her eventual milk yield is recorded, and discharged from the glass jar to be carried along a pipeline to finish up in the bulk tank.

THE CUBICLE SYSTEM

The cubicle system appeared along with milking parlours in Scotland on some farms in numbers in the late 1960s, although some were in use before that.

A cow can enter one of the single stalls when she wishes to lie down, and vacate it when she wants to. Sawdust is used for bedding as straw would choke the many pumps used during the handling of the slurry from the cubicles, to being spread on the fields.

One hundred cows are usually housed in such a system. Some farmers prefer to have their cows housed in cattle courts using straw for bedding.

DAIRY COWS

The Ayrshire cow was the most popular cow in Scotland at one time until the Friesian cow arrived on the scene around the 1940s, and eventually took over from the Ayrshire cow in many parts of the country. Dairy Shorthorn cows were very popular in Scotland at one time, but were becoming less noticeable during the 1940s. Some farmers used the Dairy Shorthorns exclusively while others had a mixture of them and Ayrshires in the milk herds. The Jersey cow was often included in many dairy herds.

The Holstein cow is now the most prominent cow in dairy farming since taking over from the Friesian cow in the 1990s.

There are still many Ayrshire, Friesian, Shorthorn and Jersey herds in the United Kingdom today.

Dairy cows have to give birth to a calf before they can produce milk and lactate for eight months to provide milk for human consumption. After this she is dried off so she can devote all her energy to producing her new calf. The newborn calf suckles its mother at least twice to ensure it receives colostrum, the first milk that contains antibodies. Those antibodies in the first milk kill or inhibit the activities of bacteria harmful to the new born calf. The calf is then separated from its mother, and fed warm milk at regular intervals from a small container with a teat attached to it. Eventually it will be put into a pen with other calves, offered solid food, and can suckle from a dispenser that supplies a warm milk substitute continually through a teat. Systems vary between some farms.

Male dairy calves generally go on to be fattened similar to beef calves as the following text will explain. The best heifer calves will join the milking herd at a later date after having their first calf when about two years old although this depends on their growth and development.

The gestation (pregnancy) mean period of nine months and the time taken for parturition (labour) in a cow is similar to that of a woman.

BEEF COWS

Beef cows or suckler cows have one calve per year or in rare cases twins. The calves suckle their mothers for about six months. The suckler cow is not bred for high yielding, long lactations. Shortly afterwards the calves will be speaned, separated from their mothers, and fed in cattle courts or continue grazing. The mature calves are eventually fattened on the same farm, or in most cases sold to farmers who specialise in fattening cattle to be sold at about two years old. Age at selling fat cattle is variable. In some enterprises most young bull calves are sold for veal meat, or as bull beef at a later stage of growth.

MULTIPLE SUCKLING

Multiple suckling takes place where a cow, usually culled from a milking herd, suckles three or four calves. She would be tethered to a stall in a byre along with other foster cows. Some of the calves would have been bought at a livestock market. Some cows might foster ten calves. Younger calves would take the place of the older calves and so on.

THE CLYDESDALE HORSE

Clydesdale horses were being used on farms and towns in Scotland up until the 1960s although there is a few Clydesdales used in some council parks in cities and towns. Clydesdale is the ancient county name for Lanarkshire. A breed of horses bearing the name originated, or came to distinction within the area embraced by the name.

Many kings both Scots and English, along with Dukes and prominent farmer breeders were involved in the breeding and improvement of the Clydesdale throughout history. Edward I of England was the first of many English Kings to impose a ban on the export of horses of military value North of the border.

The mares of the South West area of Scotland were eventually covered by Flanders stallions in the late eighteenth century to produce the horse we see today.

During its later history the Clydesdale has been exported to and continues to be bred in many parts of the world, especially the Commonwealth countries and the United States of America, making it the most popular heavy draught horse in the world.

The Clydesdale Horse Society of the United Kingdom of Great Britain and Ireland was instituted in 1877 and the publication of the retrospective volume of the Clydesdale Stud book by the society in 1878.

CHARACTERISTICS OF THE HORSE

The Clydesdale is a very active horse. It is not bred for action like the Hackney, a riding or carriage horse, but it must have action.

A Clydesdale judge uses the word with a difference. A Hackney judge using the word means high-stepping movement. A Clydesdale judge means clean lifting of the feet, not 'scliffing along', but the foot at every step must be clean off the ground, and the inside of every shoe made plain to the man standing behind.

Action for the Clydesdale judge also means 'close' movement. The fore legs must be planted well underneath the shoulders - not on the outside like the legs of a bulldog - and the legs must be plumb, hang straight from the shoulder to the fetlock joint, so to speak.

There must be no openness at the knees, and no inclination to knock the knees together. The hind legs must be planted closely together with the points of the hocks turned inwards rather than outwards; the thighs must come well down to the hocks, and the shanks from the hock joint to the fetlock joint must be plumb and straight. 'Sickle hocks' are a bad fault, as they lead to loss of leverage.

A Clydesdale judge begins to estimate the merits of a horse by examining its feet. These must be open and round, like a mason's mallet. The hoofs must be wide and springy, with no suspicion of hardness such as may lead to the formation of side bone or ringbone. The pasterns must be long, and set at an angle of 45 degrees from the hoof head to the fetlock joint. Too long a pastern is very objectionable, but very seldom seen.

A weakness to be guarded against is what is termed 'calf knees, that is the formation from the knee to the ground which begins with the knee being set back, giving an appearance of angle which is delusive, because it is not the angle from the fetlock joint to the hoof head which relieves pressure on the foot, but an angle from the knee to the hoof head which is a weakness, and unsightly.

A Clydesdale should have a nice open forehead, broad between the eyes; a flat, neither Roman-nosed nor 'dished shaped' profile, a wide muzzle, large nostrils, a bright, clear intelligent eye, a big ear, and a well arched long neck springing out of an oblique shoulder, with high withers. Its back should be short, and the ribs well sprung from the backbone like the hoops of a barrel. Its quarters should be long, and the thighs well packed with muscle and sinew. It should have broad, clean, sharply developed hocks, and big knees, broad in front. The impression created by a thoroughly well built typical Clydesdale is that of strength and activity, with a minimum of superfluous tissue. The idea is not grossness and bulk, but quality and weight.

The ideal colour for a Clydesdale is bay or brown, with a more or less defined white mark on the face, dark coloured fore legs and white hind shanks. Chestnuts are hardly ever seen among Clydesdales; blacks are a little more common now than formerly. Some roans and greys appear now and again.

HARNESS FOR A HEAVY DRAUGHT HORSE

Bridle - Head gear with blinkers.

Blinkers - Two pieces of leather. One piece fixed to either side of a bridle to prevent a horse from seeing too much.

Open bridle - Bridle without blinkers.

Bit - A thin round bar fixed to either side of the bridle that is slipped into the horse's mouth. If pulling on the reins is too severe, the horse becomes hard mouthed and therefore becomes difficult to manage.

Collar - is put over the horse's head upside down as this matches the shape of the head. After the collar passes over the horse's head it is then turned the right way up and slips down to rest on its shoulders.

Hames - Curved pieces of wood or metal that fit on either side of the collar and are coupled up by short chains at the bottom with a leather strap at the top to keep them secure. Metal hooks are fixed on the hames for draught chains to be cleeked on to.

Saddle - Sits on the horse's back and is held in place by a girth strap on the saddle. A metal bridge or groove on the saddle holds a rigwiddie chain in place that supports the cart-shafts.

Breeching - Part of the harness that goes over a horse's back and round its haunches. It enables the horse to hold back the cart going downhill, or to push the cart backwards.

Belly Band - A leather strap or piece of rope fixed on one shaft of a cart that is passed underneath the horse's belly, and made secure on the other shaft when hitching a horse to a cart. The horse becomes a counter balance if for some reason most of the load is at the rear of the cart.

Back Band - Used when ploughing for instance. It's a leather strap that hangs down either side of a pair of horses' backs, just where the saddle would sit if being used. Draught chains are fixed to them on their way from the hames hooks on the collars to the swingle trees at the rear of the horses. The reins from the horses' bridles are passed through rings attached to the back bands on to the ploughman at the rear who is controlling the plough.

Hip Strap - Carries the reins from the back band to the rear of the horse.

Spreader bar- Keeps the chains apart at the rear of a trace horse.

Martingale - Leather strap fixed to the bottom of a horse's collar, and goes through between the horse's front legs to a girth strap.

PUBERTY AND BREEDING AGE OF LIVESTOCK

The age at which puberty is reached in animals met with on the farm is roughly as given hereunder, but much may depend on breeding and feeding.

Heifer-12 to 18 months; Mare-12 to 24 months; Ewe-8 to 12 months; Gilt-4 to 5 months; Goat-8 to 12 months; Bitch-7 to 10 months; Cat-8 to 12 months.

Mares may usually be bred in their third year; Heifers at about 18 months and Gilts at 7 to 9 months, but this depends upon their development.

Oestrum (heat) periods.

Duration of Oestrum	Return after Parturation	Return after Weaning	Return if not Fertilised
Mare-5 to 7 days	7 to 10 days	....	2 to 3weeks or more
Cow- 1-day	21 to 28 days	....	3 to 4weeks or more
Ewe- 1 to 2 days	4 to 6 months	....	17 to 20 days
Sow- 2 to 4 days	....	2 to 5 days	20 to 21 days
Bitch-1 to 3 weeks	5 to 6 months	....	5 to 6 months

The seasons at which "heat" occurs are mare - February to July; goat- autumn; ewe-autumn; cow, sow, bitch and cat-all the year round.

Periods of Gestation and Incubation
(Mean or usual period in days)

Mare	340	Cat	50
Cow	283	Rabbit	28
Ewe	151	Turkey 26	
Sow	114	Hen	21
Goat	156	Duck	30
Bitch	60	Goose	30

SOME OF THE WORDS AND TERMINOLOGY ONCE USED ON FARMS IN SCOTLAND

Many of the words have become obsolete with the disappearance of the horses and the men who looked after and drove them, along with the many implements and machines that were hitched to the horses to do the jobs that varied as the seasons progressed throughout the year. It also includes the terms used by the men and women who looked after livestock, and the folk who did the orra-work, using the many hand tools required for the variety of tasks to be done during the year.

The words and terms used in Scotland, varied between counties and districts. Some of the every day words in the glossary below are spoken today.

Abin.	Above.
Afore.	Before.
Ahint.	Behind.
Ane, een, yin.	One.
Airt.	Direction.
Aits.	Oats.
Alane.	Alone.
Alow.	Below.
Anent.	Opposite, in line with.
Arles.	A token payment given to a farm worker by a farmer to seal the bargain or contract made between them.
Athoot, withoot.	Without.
Atour.	Move over.
Auld.	Old.
Ava.	At all.
Ayeweys.	Always.
Ayont.	Beyond.
Backend.	Autumn.
Backit.	Backwards.
Backside-formaist.	Back to front.
Bag.	Sack.

Barrie, barra.	Barrow.
Baist.	Beast.
Bannet, bunnet.	Bonnet.
Barkit.	Ingrained dirt.
Barnyairds.	Farm.
Battle, bottle.	Small bundle of hay or straw.
Baurly.	Barley.
Beestings.	The first milk taken from a cow after calving.
Bere awns.	Thin brittle spikes attached to grains of barley.
Besom, bizzom.	Brush, broom.
Big.	Build.
Bine.	Boyne, large round shallow container that held milk to be skimmed, and made into cream, butter or cheese.
Bing.	Heap.
Birl.	Whirl around.
Birsled.	Corn sheaves dried out by a really hot sun.
Blob.	Drop of any liquid, globular, like dew.
Boss, Kiln	Large wooden tripod built into corn stacks and hay coles to encourage the drying and maturing of the crop.
Bouman.	Bouman who looked after a bow, a herd of milk cows.
Box.	When cows head butt one another.
Braid.	Broad.
Brakfast, brekfast.	Breakfast.
Brat.	Apron made from hessian sacking.
Braw.	Fine, handsome, very good.
Brecham.	Horse's collar.
Breeks.	Trousers.
Breenge.	Rush forward recklessly.
Breer.	The first shoots of a grain crop.
Breest.	Breast.

Britching.	Breeching.
Brockit.	Animal with a white streak down its face, or having black and white stripes or spots.
Brose.	Made up of oatmeal, salt and hot water, and taken with milk.
Buchts, fank.	Pens for holding sheep, to carry out vet tasks, separating sheep, dipping and clipping etc.
Bushel.	A dry measure of capacity used in grain. A bushel of Wheat = 62lbs. (28kgs). Barley =56lbs.(25kgs). Oats=42lbs.(19kgs).
Butter brods.	A pair of wooden boards for working butter.
Byre.	Cowshed fitted with stalls.
Ca, caw.	Cart turnips from a field to the farm, for instance. Urge on cattle, to drive, or to call to someone.
Ca' awa.	Keep going.
Ca' doon.	Knock over.
Caddie or cuddie pin	Thick pin. One of two pins that fixed the bottom of a cart to the axle.
Caff.	Chaff, husks, the outer dry skin found on grains of wheat and oats. Separated from the grain whilst being threshed.
Cairt.	Cart.
Cairt-sheds.	Cart sheds. Open archways usually found underneath the granary loft. Two coup or tipping carts were housed in a bay each to be used by the horsemen and their pairs of horses. Four bays denoted the farm was a four pair place. They were expected to be able to work around between 250 and 300 acres (120 ha's). Output from a pair of horses depended if the soil was heavy, like clay or light sandy soil, and if the fields were flat or hilly. Cart-sheds can be seen on some farms at the present day.
Carsackie, carseckie.	Apron or pinafore.

Cassies, causies.	A mixture of round stones embedded in sand, provided a hard - wearing floor in a stable or a byre.
Cattler.	Cattleman.
Cauf.	Calf.
Caup.	A wooden bowl.
Claeser.	Wooden chest used by a bothy lad to keep his clothes in.
Claurt.	Smear on, a messy person.
Cleek.	Hook.
Cleg.	Horse fly.
Clocker.	Broody hen.
Coards.	Corduroy trousers.
Coop.	Small heap of dung or hay etc.
Coorse.	Course, layer of sheaves.
Coos.	Cows.
Cowt.	Colt.
Corn.	Oats or grain collectively.
Cornt.	Fed with oats.
Coupler.	Short rope tied between a pair of horses at their bridles.
Craw.	To stand on a ladder leaning against a stack being built, and fork bunches or sheaves up to it.
Cundy.	The entrance to a drain, or a covered drain.
Darg.	A day's work. It also referred to a day's ploughing or a ploughing darg given to an incoming farmer at the November term by the neighbouring farmers in the district.
Denner.	Dinner.
Double tine.	Two passes of the harrows or harrowing the field twice.
Dicht.	Wipe.
Dirl.	Ground hardening frost, or vibrating of metal when hit by a hammer.
Dirty land.	Weed infested land.

Dreel.	Drill.
Dreep.	Drip.
Dreich.	Dull, bleak or damp weather.
Drookit.	Soaked with water.
Drooth.	A thirst.
Droothy.	Good drying weather.
Dross.	Coal dust, small change in cash.
Dub.	Puddle, small pool of water.
Dumb bell.	Ornamental bell with no tongue, fixed on the peak of a horse's collar.
Dung.	Came from byres, cattle courts and stables etc. Manure or fertiliser came from sacks.
Dunt.	Strike or hit.
Easin.	Eaves. The meeting point between the shank and the head of a stack.
Ettle.	A desire, eager.
Echt, aucht.	Eight.
Feal.	Turf.
Fee.	Farm worker contracted or engaged to work for a farmer.
Fees.	A farmworker's wages, especially those paid half yearly.
Fell.	Very, as in a very steep hill or extremely cold weather.
Ferm.	Farm. Includes buildings and the surrounding land.
Fettle.	Condition, good or poor.
Fifty-sixer.	56 Ibs weight (25 kgs). Multiples used for counterbalance when weighing potatoes or grain in sacks.
Flech.	Flea.
Fleg.	Frighten.
Foggage.	Grass that grew in a field after a hay crop had been harvested from it.
Foond.	Foundation for a stack. Made of straw, stones or a stathel.

Foonert.	Condition caused by a horse or pony grazing on lush grass. It usually ends up as laminitis in the hoofs.
Forby.	Besides, in addition, as well.
Foremaist.	Foremost.
Forenent.	Opposite, in exchange for.
Forrit.	Forward.
Fower.	Four.
Frandie.	Small cone shaped stack of corn sheaves.
Furr.	Furrow.
Furr horse.	The offside horse. One of a pair hitched to a plough that walked in the furrow bottom.
Gaffer.	The grieve.
Galluses.	Trouser braces.
Gang.	Course or layer of sheaves.
Gether.	Gather.
Gibbles.	Hand tools such as shovels, hammers and saws etc.
Gey.	Of quantity, considerable, as in a gey number of folk or a gey steep hill.
Girned.	Of ploughing. Gaps showing between ploughed furrows.
Glaur.	Mud.
Graip.	Short wooden shaft with a handle at one end and four or five tines fitted at the other end.
Graith.	Implements and machinery.
Grauvat, gravat.	Scarf or piece of cloth tied round the neck.
Greaser.	Dungaree jacket.
Green holin'	Harvesting potatoes when the haulms are still green.
Gress.	Grass.
Groothie.	Good plant growing weather.
Gruip.	The dung channel in a byre.
Grund.	Ground, earth or soil.
Gushet.	Triangular piece of land.
Gussie.	A young pig.
Gutters.	Mud.
Hacklog.	Large round thick log used as a base for splitting

	wood on with an axe.
Hairst.	Harvest.
Half-roond.	Half-round, one length of the field.
Hamestead.	Farm.
Happer.	Hopper.
Harle.	A broad, deep hoe for scraping mud around the farm.
Harvest home dance.	Held in the granary loft soon after the completion of the grain harvest. The granary was made ready after much sweeping, and decorating with bunting etc. Music was provided by a melodeon player and a fiddler.
Hashed.	Of turnips, sliced or chipped to be fed to livestock.
Haunle.	Handle.
Haik.	Heck. A rack, a slatted iron or wooden framework for holding hay or straw.
Heel.	The remains of a stack still to be loaded on to a cart.
Herness.	Harness.
Headin' oot.	Building the head of a stack.
Heavy.	The side of a stack is angled out past the perpen -dicular.
Hefted.	Cow needing milked.
Hert, hertnin'.	Heart or core of a stack. A gang of hertnin˙ was built well above the height of the outside gang on a stack.
Het.	Hot.
Hey.	Hay.
Hey seed barrie.	Grass seed broadcaster.
Hing.	Hang or slope of the outside gang of sheaves on a stack, This prevented water seeping into the stack.
Hoggets or hoggs.	Young sheep never been sheared, fed for fattening.
Horse, horses.	On most farms in Scotland, the plural of a horse or somethings was denoted by the number preceding it. For instance a pair o' horse, two load of turnips and the ten acre field.
Howk.	To dig soil over using a graip.

Hurl.	A ride in a cart or to push a wheelbarrow.
Inower.	Inside, within, over and in.
Jaikit, jeckit.	Jacket.
Jibber.	A horse unwilling to pull. There could be a reason such as a sore shoulder.
Jootered up.	Polished. Of harness or a tractor.
Keb.	Ewe aborting, so producing a dead lamb.
Kenlin.	Kindling, small pieces of split wood used to light a coal fire.
Kist.	Chest, a large wooden box with a lid.
Knee.	The bend on a coulter stang or stem.
Knot grass.	Grass with knotty stems.
Knowe.	Hill top or knoll.
Kye.	Cows.
Kye time.	Milking time.
Land or hand horse.	The nearside horse. One of a pair hitched to a plough.
Leading.	Carting hay or sheaves of corn from a field to be built into stacks at the farm.
Ledder.	Ladder.
Leggums.	Leggings. Made from sacking or canvas. It was wrapped round the ankles or around the legs up to below the knees, and tied tightly with binder twine. The leggums kept the trouser bottoms free of mud.
Ley.	Lea, grassland.
Light, bare, grippit.	A side of a stack is angled in past the perpendicular.
Loose box.	Part of a stable or byre for an un-tethered animal.
Loupit, lowpit.	Leapt, jumped.
Lousin'.	Unhitching the horses from the plough etc.
Lousin' time.	Stopping time at work.
Luggie.	Pail with an upright handle that extended about six inches above the rim. The luggie was held between the knees while a person sat on a stool milking a cow. The luggie held about three gallons

	(13.5 litres) of milk.
Maidie, kitchie deem.	Farmhouse maid.
Mairch.	March. Boundary fence, dyke or hedge.
Manyir.	Manure or fertiliser.
Manyir barrie.	Fertiliser spreader.
Mauch, mauk.	Maggot.
Mauch flea.	Bluebottle.
Maukit.	Filthy with maggots, especially sheep.
Maun.	Must.
Mealer.	Wooden chest used by a bothy lad to keep his food, crockery and cutlery in.
Micht.	Might.
Mid-yokin', midsir.	Ploughman's tea and piece taken in the middle of the forenoon.
Mochie.	Close, warm, or moist atmosphere.
Mole heaps.	Small clamps of swedes that were sliced or chipped and fed to fattening sheep during the winter and spring.
Morn.	Morning.
Morn's morn.	Tomorrow morning.
Morn's nicht.	Tomorrow evening.
Muck hawk.	Dung hak. Has a long shaft with four tines set at right angles to it at one end.
Muckle, meiklc.	Applied to the larger of two farms with the same name.
Muckle.	Much, a great deal.
Muggie.	Drizzling, wet, misty and warm.
Muntin.	Mounting. Ornamental metal or brass fitting fixed to a horse's harness, or new parts fitted to a plough.
Murky.	Gloomy, dark.
Mull.	Mill.
Neep.	Turnip.
Neep barrie.	Turnip seeder. At one time, fertiliser, turnip and grass seed were sown by a man pushing a wheel barrow type frame, fitted with either a seed box

	to hold turnip seed or a long hopper to hold grass seed or fertiliser.
Neep pit.	Turnip clamp.
Nicky tams.	Leather straps adorned with small pieces of harness
Wull tams.	muntin' which were buckled around the legs just
Knee belts.	below the knees. They kept the trouser bottoms clear of mud and also the inside of the knees free of cloth, especially when walking along the bottom of a furrow when ploughing, or when doing row crop work with a pair of horses.
Orders.	Jobs to be done.
Orra.	Applied to a man who did a variety of jobs on a farm. It was also used to describe a horse which didn't belong a pair.
Oxter.	Armpit.
Pannie.	Kindling wood or a bothy lad doing his week on pannie.
Pendicle.	Small holding.
Perr.	Pair.
Pint.	Point, the tapering part of a field.
Pitawtie, tattie, tottie.	Potato.
Ploo.	Plough.
Powk.	Dig or excavate.
Praps.	Props. Four of them were set in below the eaves around a stack before it was completed, and after completion they were tightened or slackened where required, so as to encourage the stack to settle down evenly.
Pu'.	Pull.
Puckle.	Small amount.
Pund.	Pound weight.
Pyot.	Man who passes sheaves or bunches of straw to a man building the stack.
Quey.	Heifer. Applied mostly to a dairy heifer.
Quoil.	Small heap of hay.

Raik.	As much of anything that will make a load.
Raip.	Rope.
Raivelt.	Muddled, tangled.
Rance.	Wooden stay used to assist in keeping strainer upright in a wire fence.
Rank.	Tall and strong as in a growing crop of corn.
Raw.	Row or line of corn stacks etc.
Raw.	Damp and cold or undiluted.
Rax.	Over exert, strain.
Redd.	Clear a space, make room.
Ridlan.	Redland. Land cleared of potatoes or turnips.
Reed, court.	Large shed where cattle are housed.
Reest, reist.	The mould board of a plough.
Rig.	Strip of ploughed land etc.
Rines, lines.	Reins.
Roond.	A round. Travel two lengths of a field. Up to one end and back.
Roup.	Farm sale of livestock, implements and machinery etc. owned by the out going farmer, usually at the November term.
Routh.	Plenty, an abundance of anything.
Row-crop work.	Harrowing, grubbing and furrowing up, and ridging the potato drills. Also horse-hoeing the turnip drills.
Rowst (as in cow).	Arouse, stir to move.
Rug.	Pull forcibly.
Sair.	Sore.
Saut.	Salt.
Sax.	Six.
Skail.	Spill.
Scart.	Scratch.
Sclaffed.	Shallow furrow thrown over on its back.
Scrapit.	Scraped.
Scud.	Sudden shower of rain.
Scull, skep.	Scooped shaped basket made of wicker, used for

	carrying turnips etc.
Scythe.	Made up of a three and half feet (10.2cms) curved blade attached to a wooden shank or sned which branched out to give two handles at waist level.
Seck barrie.	Sack barrow used for carrying sacks full of grain. It was loaded vertically then tilted backwards. A thick metal plate at the bottom of the barrow between the small wheels supported the sack while the barrow was being pushed.
Seeven.	Seven.
Shaif.	Sheaf,
Shairn.	Dung direct from a cow.
Shairps.	Frost nails on a horse's shoe.
Shank.	Main part of a stack. The sides or walls.
Shawin' neeps.	Cutting the shaws and roots off turnips. Topping and tailing.
Shaws.	Haulms, the stalks and leaves of turnips and potatoes.
Sheckle.	Linkage which connects the plough beam to the main or master swingle tree.
Shog.	Shake.
Shoorgoon.	Short gown worn by a farmhouse maid at work.
Shouther.	Shoulder.
Shuil, shiel.	A shovel or shovel earth.
Sic.	Such.
Sidlan.	Side-land, sloping piece of ground.
Sile.	Soil.
Skelloch, skellie.	Charlock, a weed belonging to the mustard family.
Skite.	Slip or slide on a slippery surface.
Slag.	Large forkful of hay or a good graipful of dung.
Slap.	Gap in a hedge, fence or dyke.
Sleekit.	Smooth, shiny, crafty.
Smeek.	Smoke, fumigate.
Smoor, smuir.	Smother, put out.
Smur.	Drizzle or light rain.

Sneck.	Latch for keeping door or gate shut.
Snell.	Severe as in cold weather. Neat and tidy.
Soo.	Large straw stack built from bunches being made by a threshing mill.
Soor.	Sour.
Soordook.	Butter milk.
Spartie.	Esparto grass rope made from a coarse grass native to Spain and North Africa. It wasn't as strong as sisal rope made from sisal grass, but was ideal for roping down thatch on corn stacks, and making hay coles or rucks secure.
Spean, spane.	Wean. To take calves, lambs or piglets away from their mothers. Terminate suckling.
Spuin.	Spoon.
Spurtle.	Short stick for stirring porridge.
Staiger.	Horseman who broke in horses to carting and chains. He might have had to look after a stallion or stallions.
Sta' collar.	Leather collar that was fastened to a rope at one end while the other end was tied to a wooden sinkerball. The rope slipped up and down through a ring fixed to the manger while the horse was feeding from the manger or a hay heck.
Stathels.	Round frames of wood or iron for building large wheat stacks on.
Stibble.	Stubble.
Stilts.	Handles for controlling a plough.
Strae.	Straw.
Steens, stanes.	Stones.
Stracht.	Straight.
Straik o' the harries.	One pass of the harrows.
Stoor.	Dust.
Stores.	Animals kept for fattening.
Suckler.	A beef cow that suckles a calf.
Tackety buits.	Hobnailed boots.

Taft.	Toft, farm.
Tapner.	A curved knife with a hooked tip. Used for topping and tailing turnips.
Tathe.	Dung left on ground where sheep had been feeding on turnips.
Tattie pit.	Potato clamp.
Tattie herp.	Potato harp. Potato graip with ball points on ends of tines.
Tuim, tume.	Empty, empty out.
Teuch.	Tough.
Teuchat storm.	A period of bleak wintry weather in late March when the lapwings, sometimes called teuchats came to nest on the ploughed fields.
Theek, thaick.	Thatch. Usually wheat straw put on the heads of corn and hay stacks to keep them free of rain and snow.
Theets, theats.	Trace chains used by a horse to assist another horse pulling a cart.
Theeter, theater.	A trace horse.
Thibet.	Apron worn by farm maids. The cloth was made from a fine wool.
Thin.	As in winds, piercing or wanting to go through a person.
Thole.	Endure.
Tie backs.	Two short ropes crossed tied between a pair of horses from the bridle of each horse to a ring on their partner's back-band.
Toby.	Stopcock on a water pipe.
Torr-bane.	The prominence on the pelvic bone of a cow.
Toosled.	Tousled. Tangled or unkempt.
Trams.	Shafts of a cart.
Travis.	Treviss. A partition between stalls in a stable or byre.
Treckin, trickin.	A journey into town with a horse and cart or tractor and trailer to collect grass seed, or deliver corn to a seed merchant, or collect repaired canvases for the binders from the saddlers.

Trink.	Trench or ditch.
Tusk.	To empty contents from one bag into another one.
Twa.	Two.
Twa or three.	Some.
Wabbit.	Exhausted, tired out.
Wark.	Work.
Wat, weet.	Wet.
Wecht.	Weight.
Weskit, wastcoat.	Waistcoat.
Wey.	Weigh.
Whate.	Wheat.
Wheen.	Quite a number. A wheen o'folk.
Windy.	Proud, boastful.
Wrack.	Couch grass.
Yaince.	Once.
Yaise.	Use.
Yark.	Wrench. To exert oneself.
Yeuky.	Itchy.
Yokin.	Half-days work.
Yokit	Folk working or horses hitched to a plough or cart.
Yokit double.	When a horseman had his pair of horses pulling one cart. One horse was hitched to the cart while the other one was used as a trace horse.
Yokit single.	When a horseman had his pair of horses hitched to a cart each.
Yowe (as in cow).	Ewe.

WEATHER LORE

March winds and April showers,
Bring forth May flowers.

A red sky at night,
Is the shepherd's delight.
A red sky in the morning,
Is the shepherd's warning.

Be it dry or wet,
The weather will always pay its debt.
The weather always equals itself out.

Ne'er cast a cloot,
Till May be oot.
May applies to the month not the flower of the Hawthorn.

94

Rain before seven,
Fair before eleven.

Rain from the East,
Will last three days at least.

When the wind is in the West,
 Then the wind is at its best.

When the wind is in the East,
'Tis neither good for man nor beast.

If the Oak is out before the Ash,
Then you'll only get a splash.

But if the Ash beats the Oak,
Then you can expect a soak.

After a few days of rime,
Rain follows every time.

When the stars huddle,
The earth will soon puddle.

Clear moon. Frost soon.

If March comes in like a lion,
 It goes out like a lamb.
If it comes in like a lamb,
It goes out like a lion.

A dry May and dripping June,
Brings everything in tune.

Dew in the night,
Next day will be bright.
Grey mists at dawn,
The day will be warm.

A blink before a drink.
A short spell of sunshine before a
shower of rain.

As the day lengthens,
So the cauld strengthens.

When the snaw hings aboot,
There's mair tae come, nae doot.

February will fill dyke,
Black or white.
Dyke is another name for a ditch. It
will be filled with either water or snow.

If in February there is no rain,
'Tis neither good for hay or grain.

It's caulder in the thaw,
Than in the snaw.

Ice in November to bear a duck,
The rest of winter will be slush and muck.

If the birds begin to sing in January,
Frosts are on the way.

March in January,
January in March.

So many mists in March.
So many frosts in May.

A peck of March dust,
Is worth a king's ransom.

Beware of an Oak,
It draws the stroke.
Avoid an Ash,
It courts a flash.
Creep under the Thorn.
Advice on where to shelter during a thunder storm.

95

Sound travelling far in the night,
A rainy day it will betide.

September blow soft,
Till the fruit's in the loft.

When you can step on six daisies at once,
Summer has come.

A swarm of bees in May,
Is worth a load of hay.

A swarm of bees in June,
Is worth a silver spoon.

A swarm of bees in July,
Is not worth a fly.

Evening red and morning grey,
Two good signs for one fine day.

Evening grey and morning red,
Sends the shepherd wet to bed.

If the evening be grey and the morning red,
The lamb and ewe will go wet to bed.

If the sun goes pale to bed,
'Twill rain tomorrow it is said.

If the cock goes crowing to bed,
He'll certainly rise with a watery head.

If a fly lands on your nose,
Swat it till it goes.
If the fly then lands again,
It will bring back heavy rain.

If the woolly fleeces strew the heavenly way,
Be sure no rain disturbs the summer day.

A January spring is worth nothing.

Thunder in March.
Floods in May.

On the first of Merch,
The crows begin to search.
The crows look for a mate, and twigs to build a nest.

Long foretold, long past.
Short notice, soon past.

A sunny shower,
Won't last half an hour.

You may shear your sheep,
When the Elder blossoms peep.

The Cuckoo comes in April,
He sings his song in May.
In the middle of June he changes
his tune. And in July he flies away.

Pale moon does rain.
Red moon does blow.
White moon does neither rain nor snow.

A foot deep of rain,
Will kill hay and grain.
But three feet of snow,
Will make them grow mo'

If it rains on Easter day,
There'll be good grass, but very bad hay.

Near ring, far rain.
Far ring, near rain.
Ring is the halo round the moon.

96

Mackeral sky, mackeral sky.
Never long wet, never long dry.

A rain topped cloud with flattened base,
Carries raindrops on its face.

A rainbow at night,
Fair weather in sight.
A rainbow at dawn,
Fair weather all gone.

If the grass grows in January,
It grows the worse for the year.

Easter in snow, Christmas in mud.
Christmas in snow, Easter in mud.

A dry Lent means a fertile year.

A leak in June
Sets the corn in tune.

When the clouds appear like rocks
and towers.
The earth will be refreshed by frequent
showers.

WEATHER LORE
Effect of weather on animals, birds, insects and plants.

Pigs can see the wind is sometimes quoted. They do become very agitated when strong winds are on the way. They toss the straw about with their snouts when confined to pens.

Cats become anxious when gales are due to arrive. They usually hole up some place until the weather improves. They wash fastidiously behind their ears when rain is imminent.

Most animals dislike winds. Some work- horses are not happy working in windy conditions.

Cows come off the high ground when thunder and rain is on the way.

When swallows fly low to feed on insects, it is a sign of rain or thunder. When feeding much higher, weather is going to be more settled.

Most creatures if not all, are attuned to varying weather conditions, and therefore are reliable weather forecasters.

Many plants are good weather forecasters.

Trees that are not usually classed along with vegetable plants are also good weather indicators. An example is when their leaves show their undersides. It's a sign of rain. Some trees are more exhibiting than others.

Cattle

When a cow tries to scratch its ear,
It means a shower is very near.
When it clumps its side with its tail,
Look out for thunder, lightning and hail.

Bees

When the bees crowd out of their hive,
The weather makes it good to be alive.
When the bees crowd into their hive again,
It is a sign of thunder and rain.

Flowers

When Scarlet Pimpernels' petals open,
Sunny weather is sure to happen.
But when the rain is on its way,
Their petals close for the rest of the day.

Weather and Religion

Candlemas day 2nd February.

If Candlemas day be fair and bright,
Winter will have another flight.
But if Candlemas day be clouds and rain,
Winter is gone and will not come again.

St. Swithin's Day 15th July.

Oh! St. Swithin if thou'll be fair,
For forty days shall rain nae mair.
But if St. Swithin's thou be wet,
For forty days it raineth yet.